STRAWBERRY GROWING

STRAWBERRY GROWING

D Macer Wright

DAVID & CHARLES
Newton Abbot

0 7153 5755 7

Set in 11/13 Baskerville
and printed in Great Britain
by W J Holman Ltd Dawlish
for David & Charles (Holdings) Limited
South Devon House Newton Abbot Devon

Contents

Illustrations

LINE DRAWINGS

Drawings by N. S. Hyslop

Introduction

All the world loves a strawberry. No fruit is more highly prized, more delightedly consumed. Strawberries are always a treat, never more so than when home grown and gathered sweet and fragrant from garden plot, greenhouse or frame, or from hanging basket, gaily painted wheelbarrow, window box or flowerpot. Even an old hollow tree stump can be fitted with a wire basket and turned into a perfect home for a Frapendula strawberry, cropping heavily from the main plant and sending out fruiting tendrils to give a bonus crop and to decorate the stump. And more than once gardeners have astonished their neighbours with prize winning early berries grown under jam jars.

There is no need to regard strawberries as an impossible luxury; no fruit is more adaptable and there really is no mystique about growing it. Anybody can grow good, professional looking strawberries in the garden if they are prepared to take in a few basic essentials, for the fruit is not an exotic needing endless finicky treatment, but a cultivated form of a wild plant that, in its natural habitat, grows like a weed.

The key to success is the correct timing of certain highly important measures, though some are not necessary every year. In wet weather, prevention of the horrible greymould disease demands exact timing of three or four simple sprays, though these are seldom needed in dry weather. Watering must be done at specific stages of growth, and not simply when the fancy moves us. Plants should not be kept for years on end, becoming scrappier and scrappier and giving poorer crops of seedy little berries with each passing season. We can keep gooseberry bushes in good crop for a decade or more, but strawberries are not gooseberry bushes, though many people seem to think they have the same life.

Usually, three cropping seasons are enough for the summer

9

fruiters, though a quick in-and-out policy often pays dividends, planting in early August, getting a bumper crop the following year, and then replacing with new plants again planted in August. This is certainly a sound method with the perpetuals, which crop heavily in their first year, if planted early, but tend to fall off later.

Strawberries often present a challenge. Our soil may not be ideal, but there are few soils that cannot be brought up to standard with good compost correctly used. It may be too wet, in which case we can overcome the trouble by ridge culture; perhaps we have no space for growing and rotating strawberries—and rotation is a basic need; even so, there are those window boxes and flower pots or a tub or water butt.

Even if it is only for some special occasion that falls due in the strawberry season, we can all have a dish of splendid berries. One gardener I know never fails to present his wife with a strawberry tea on her birthday. It is a simple gesture, perhaps, and costs him little in cash, but for his wife it is the highlight of the year.

In the pages that follow I have tried to give a reasonably comprehensive account of amateur strawberry growing. Practice is based on principle; we must know not only what we are doing, but why we do it, so I have dealt first with principles and then with practice but the two are sufficiently separate to enable readers to attack the practical aspects first, if they wish.

I have drawn freely on modern research and experimental work but have mentioned only general source references, partly because detailed ones would be out of place in a book for amateurs, and partly because they would not be of much help, since research papers are not readily available to home gardeners.

I hope that such mildly scientific and technical treatment as the pages embrace will not be dismissed as mere theory. There is in gardening a tendency, both brisk and endearing, to reject anything that smells of the test-tube. Up to a point this is understandable, for there are plenty of gardeners who

produce first class crops without consulting a scientific trea-
tise in their lives. But even they, or their plants, are the
victims of science, or its beneficiaries, whichever way we
regard it, for the gardeners' results are due in no small
measure to devoted men and women who spend their lives
peering through microscopes, probing into the mysteries of
genes and chromosomes, tinkering with tweezers and petri
dishes, and sometimes confounding in months notions wrongly
held for generations.

PART I

I

Botanical

THE FLOWER

The five petals of the strawberry flower are white in the cultivated varieties and also mainly in the wild, though yellow
ones are sometimes found among wild species. There are five
large sepals alternating with five smaller ones to form the
epicalyx. There are numerous stamens, and in modern cultivated varieties the flowers are perfect, combining staminate
(male) with pistillate (female) organs, but in the wild, single-
sex flowers only may occur.

The plant ripens a succession of crops over a period varying
between days and months, depending on whether the variety
is a summer fruiter or a so-called perpetual. This habit arises
as a result of a clearly defined pattern of flower bud formation, or to use the more precise technical term, inflorescence
initiation. We need this term to distinguish the formation of
floral organs within the bud from the appearance in spring
of the fully formed flowers.

The flowers are called primary, secondary, tertiary and so
on, in order of their initiation. First there is the elongating
shoot, or vegetative growing point. This is not a shoot in the
sense of being a growing twig, as in the case of a tree, but a
short, blunt and slightly domed organ, which produces leaf
primordia around itself in spiral succession. These give rise
to leaf stalks and leaves, and the growing point slightly elon-
gates at this stage, which marks the beginning of inflorescence
initiation. The point then becomes flatter and embryonic
sepals form round its top. Subsequent floral initiation proceeds in the order of petals, stamens and pistils.

Finally, the first flowers, or primaries, are initiated, and the
completed structure is known as the crown.

Just below this a secondary crown extension develops, on

which the secondary flowers form, and more crowns and flowers occur in sequence.

There are roughly seven to ten days between the full initiation of each set of flowers. The time of initiation of primaries
varies somewhat according to variety, and is not necessarily
the same for any given variety everywhere, since climatic factors will influence growth rate.

As a general guide, primary flowers of Royal Sovereign
should be at the immediate pre-initiation stage in early
September; a week later sepal initials should have formed.
On Climax the process may start considerably earlier, perhaps in mid-July. Early formed runners of Royal Sovereign
will form flower initials at about the same time as the parent
plant, while runners rooting in September should initiate
primary flower primordia soon after rooting.

Differentiation—ie the determination of the habit of a
bud, whether vegetative or flowering, is the first step in this
growth cycle. To a marked degree the differentiation of buds
into flowering points can be influenced in fruit culture by
pruning, feeding and other measures. Leaf and crown growth
and inflorescence initiation proceed in strawberries in the
growing season, and by the onset of winter a good plant will
have several crowns, the number depending on its age. The
largest number of strong, productive crowns is probably
reached in the second or third year, often the second, which
points to the fact that after the third fruiting season the yield
of the best quality berries will decline. Thus plants retained
beyond this age are not paying their way, and it is less economical to persist with them than it is to replace them, either
with the best of their runners, or with new stock.

Each crown will have its complement of flower buds. Some
varieties possibly form additional flowers on these crowns in
the following spring; others, like Royal Sovereign and Climax
normally do not, but start to produce new crowns in spring
from buds just below the previous year's primary flowers.

The onset of winter does not, of course, find the plant at a
stage where all flower buds have reached complete formation.

Page 17 Picking strawberries

Page 18 Barrel cultivation

This stage should have been reached on the earliest formed crowns, on which the subsequent growth pattern of flower initiation has been completed, but lower down on the plant, buds will have been developing as branch crowns, and these, being the latest to form, will be in an earlier stage.

This 'downward pattern' of new growth is typical of the habit known as sympodial, which is common to various plant species. When a growing point differentiates into an inflorescence, as in the strawberry, it ceases to extend, and the lateral bud immediately below it is stimulated into growth. This explains, at least, to some extent, the dwarfed or sometimes flattened nature of the strawberry plant, for new growth never springs out in upward progression, to make the plant taller, but in lower, from points below the apices of crowns, except among certain perpetuals that grow upwards in tiers of crowns.

In strawberry plants the stimulated lateral buds grow out as leaf stalks and leaves. Within the axils of some of these, ie the junctions of leaf stalks with the members from which they grow, will lie another bud which will start as a growing point and will then differentiate into an inflorescence in the manner already described.

In spring, the fully differentiated flower buds will open and flowers will emerge in the primary, secondary etc order in which they were formed on the crowns, and in accordance with successive crown growth. Generally, the largest berries arise from primary trusses, and the smallest from later ones. This is expressed as a gradual diminution in berry size as the fruiting season advances, as far as conventional summer fruiting types are concerned, though it may be less marked, or may scarcely apply, to the latest huge berry types from the continent.

This is a very sketchy account of a complex subject which received detailed investigation some twenty years ago by C. G. Guttridge of Long Ashton Research Station, aided by colleagues from other research establishments. The process I have outlined is obviously subject to variation according to

B

the degree to which weather and cultural standards influence growth. The basis of the plant's fruiting potential is the number of crowns it can make, and this is determined by those various elements we lump together as 'growing conditions'. Our own cultural measures should be included in this term; everyone blames the weather when things go wrong, but this is just as silly as taking all the credit when things go right, though it must be admitted that the weather can sometimes reduce the most skilful gardener's efforts to naught.

THE FRUIT

Although we speak of each individual strawberry as a fruit, this is a term of convenience rather than of botany. The swollen, fleshy part we eat is the receptacle, and the so-called seeds embedded on its surface are the fruits. These are correctly known as achenes, and each one contains a seed. Full seed development is necessary for perfectly formed berries, since receptacle formation is governed by the release of a hormone from the seeds that stimulates the swelling of the receptacle. Thus where seeds are poor, some distortion of the berry will occur in their immediate vicinity. It is a very simple matter to confirm this; examination through a good lens of a malformed or sunken area will reveal that the achenes in that area are shrivelled in some degree. Shrivelled achenes denote shrivelled seeds, since the former will not grow if the latter are dead. There may of course be some other reason for berry malformation, a subject we will consider in more detail later, but where the reason is poor seed growth, the relationship between this and the malformed area will be evident.

THE LEAF

The leaf is compound, generally of three leaflets (trifoliate) and toothed. Occasionally four or five leaflets occur. Leaflet shape may vary slightly, but is typically ovate. Leaflets are not, in the botanical sense, immature leaves. They are the components of a compound leaf, which consists of varying numbers of leaflets according to the plant. The oak leaf, for example, is single, and so is the daisy leaf, which shows how the huge and the tiny can share a characteristic. Such leaves are called simple. Like that of the strawberry, the ash leaf is compound, being composed of several leaflets.

Leaflets on strawberry plants arise as a rosette at the tip of the leaf stalk (petiole). Botanists distinguish the main leaf or leaflet structure by the name of leaf blade or lamina, and the venation as reticulate or parallel. In the strawberry there is a mid-rib, from which branch veins arise, and from these, secondary ones, to give a net-like or reticulate arrangement.

Leaf veins are channels for conducting water and dissolved substances into the leaves, these having come from the soil via the roots, and also for conducting the foodstuffs manufactured from these substances away from the leaf and into other channels, alsong which they are carried to the entire plant.

Leaves are the plant's factory in which, by the aid of carbon dioxide from the air, the process of photosynthesis is carried on. This is essentially a manufacturing process; the dissolved substances drawn into the leaves from the soil are raw materials only. In that state they cannot feed the plant. But once in the leaf they are, by the action of sunlight on the chlorophyll content of the leaf, ie the green colouring matter, turned into the finished foods, which are then translocated to every part of the plant.

We need not go any further into the botany of the strawberry leaf, but it is pertinent to say here that the efficient working of this factory is indispensable to the well-being of the plant. If leaves are not functioning properly, the plant will suffer. That is quite inevitable, though the degree of distress may vary between the severe and the slight, reflecting the extent to which the efficiency of the foliage has been reduced.

Essentially, all plant distress is a matter of starvation. No matter what the cause of the distress—pests, diseases, wind damage, drought, floods—the ultimate effect is to deny the plant its food. This is not always appreciated, and because it is not, we can easily overlook the vital need for healthy leaves, and also the equally vital need for healthy roots.

THE ROOT

We might start our consideration of strawberry roots by bearing in mind that the soil area exploited by the roots of a thriving plant is, relatively speaking, quite considerable. When C. E. T. Mann and E. Ball of the Long Ashton Research Station, carried out their classical studies in root and shoot growth of strawberries, 1924-6, they found that in order to lift plants for root examination without causing root damage, it was necessary to lift with a cylinder of soil 18-24in in diameter, and about 12in deep. This meant a cylinder which extended slightly beyond the outermost leaves; very few roots penetrated beyond this limit, but as a flourishing plant can have many crowns in its second or third year, with the attendant foliage mass, it is clear that its circumference will define an appreciable lateral zone of roots, while the circumference of a smaller plant will define a smaller equally related zone.

But whatever the age and size of the plant, most of its root system will be in the top 6in of soil. On a good loam, a two-year plant of Royal Sovereign of average growth will have about 90% of its roots in this region. Roughly 70% will be in the top 3in, and 20% in the next 3in. The remainder are sparsely distributed throughout the next 10in or so.

There is also a fairly distinct pattern of root distribution in the top 6in. Mann and Ball found approximately 25% of roots in the top inch, 21% in the second inch, 26% in the third, and 18% from the third down to the sixth.

We should appreciate, however, that although this root distribution may be taken as a general pattern, there can be a much greater length of roots where vigorous modern varieties are grown on deep land. For example, two-year plants of Cambridge Vigour have been found to have quantities of roots as deep as 18in, with some extending to 42in. One-year plants in the same soil had made almost as extensive a root system at ten months, though with less density.

One practical aspect of root distribution is that if we hoe even in to the top inch of soil underneath the leaf canopy, we shall endanger, and possibly severely damage, nearly a quarter of the plants' entire root system.

The root mass consists partly of primary roots formed mainly in summer and autumn from the base of new crowns. The part of the plant from which roots arise is the hard, thick area below the crown, and is known as the rhizome. Root development follows the same sympodial arrangement that we have already discussed, but with the actual root origins following a downward progression, in accordance with crown development. Thus as 'daughter' crowns arise in downward series below the original one, so do new roots arise in the same series.

From these, secondaries and laterals spring, which bear the fine, hairy 'feeding' roots. The term feeding roots is accepted as convenient and self-explanatory, though 'absorbing' is more accurate, since roots do not feed, but absorb nutrient solutions from the soil—our raw materials—which are translocated to the leaves to undergo the manufacturing process. Except for carbon, which is taken in by the leaves from the air, all the nutrients are absorbed in solution from the soil.

A point of considerable importance about root origins is that although crowns are formed in a downward pattern, and to this extent we can say that new roots follow the same pattern, in fact new roots on each crown base, or rhizome, actually occur from points above the old ones. The practical significance of this relates to planting depth and to the necessity at all times to avoid crown exposure.

When new roots form they must make immediate contact with the soil, and the soil must obviously be in a fit condition to receive them. If an examination of plants which have been disturbed round the crown bases by hoeing is made, or an examination of plants not set deeply enough, it will often be found that there are small tufts of aborted roots which have failed to penetrate the soil.

Similarly with the runners or stolons, which normally root to provide 'runner plants' for propagation. If their lowest leaves are removed, small white points will be exposed. These are root primordia which push out into the soil. But if the runners are too far above the soil surface the roots will not grow.

Root and top growth of strawberries follow a definite pattern. In late summer, about the beginning of August, new crowns and primary roots begin to form. Root progress is relatively slow at first, while crowns are developing, but increases from about mid August, when it becomes and remains vigorous throughout autumn.

During winter there is a period of virtual dormancy. If things have gone well there will now be good primaries together with their feeding roots. In spring and early summer there will be vigorous shoot growth and also strong development of the feeding roots formed the previous autumn, though not a great deal of newly originating roots. The late summer and autumn see a return to new crown and new primary root formation.

The vital period in this cycle is that which extends after harvest until dormancy. The progress of the plants, whether established cropping ones or new ones bought for planting, or runners removed from parent plants, depends fundamentally on the roots formed during this period.

Poor root growth at this time nearly always means poor crowns and leaves the following year, which of course mean disappointing crops. This is basically why it is so important to get new plants in early, so as to give them every chance of making the vital autumn root growth, if a first season's crop is wanted the year after planting.

If we delay planting until September, we shall disturb the roots just when these are at the peak of their development. This is unavoidable, even when merely transferring our own runners. When the plants have travelled from a nursery, no matter how carefully they were lifted and packed, the time spent out of the soil is bound to lessen still further the plants' chances of establishment in time for cropping the next season. This does not apply to plants rooted and grown in composition pots. In their case there is no disturbance, since the plants are despatched in the pots, and are planted *in situ* by the gardener.

There is plenty of evidence from experimental work showing that plants set out in September may carry only half the crop the following year of those set out in August. Furthermore, there is the possibility of a chain reaction resulting from premature cropping, which could lead to weakened plants even in the second year. If they were kept for a third season, the chances of a final bumper yield to compensate for two poor seasons would not be great. There is at least one record of the total first year's crop on August set plants of Royal Sovereign being three and a half to four times that of September planted ones. There is also evidence of the fact that the single season's yield from early set plants can be greater than the three-year total from plants set in autumn and cropped the following spring.

As we have just seen, there is a spurt of root growth in mid August. Even at this relatively early date, therefore, transplanting will interfere with the roots, for no sooner will they have got going than they will be checked. Since the impetus lies just behind the tip, or root cap, as a result of growth substances or hormones being concentrated in that area, any breakage of root tips consequent upon lifting, will leave the roots temporarily without the stimulant to growth. Fresh hormones will have to be formed and re-concentrated at the growing tip, and the later this occurs, the less the likelihood of vigorous roots and crowns becoming established during the autumn.

Thus the latest period for planting or transplanting consistent with the least disturbance to rapidly growing roots is before mid August. In some seasons late July is the best time.

If, however, circumstances are against early planting, then ordinary summer fruiting varieties planted in autumn should be de-blossomed the following spring.

The advent of composition pots which gradually disintegrate in the soil has, of course, greatly helped private gardeners and nurserymen. We will discuss the rooting of runners later, but this is a convenient point to mention that if this type of pot is used for home propagation, the question of actual root disturbance is less important, but the need for early transplanting still exists, because we do not want to leave the rooted runners in the close confines of the strawberry bed any longer than we must. The sooner they are transplanted into the more open conditions of the new bed, the sooner will they get established.

THE RUNNERS (STOLONS)

The runners are the plant's natural method of perpetuation. They are, in effect, prostrate shoots or branches, along which roots and leaves form at intervals to make new plants, each runner being capable of developing several offspring.

It is possible that the potential performance of runners in relation to their appearance in the bed is mis-understood by amateurs, and this can be the primary reason for delaying transplanting beyond the ideal time.

The essential point to appreciate is that once early rooted runners, ie those nearest the parent plants, have established initial roots they soon become self-supporting, even though they may not look very robust. But if we wait until many later runners have formed before we transplant, then competition will be such that the young plants may fail to attain vigour, and they may continue to show some degree of weakness after they have been transplanted. Furthermore, the longer they are left, the greater will be the eventual root disturbance.

So often the progress of runners is judged by crown growth; if this is poor, transplanting is delayed, in the hopes that crown growth will improve. In fact, this is literally getting the thing upside down. It is not the crowns that matter, but the roots. By the time the latter are established, but before the real growth surge has started, and the runners are ready for cutting off and transplanting, the crowns may be only half developed. But they will continue to develop in their new quarters, and by the end of the season there may be three or four good crowns on each plant.

The cycle of root and top growth on transplanted runners is similar to that on established plants. I do not want to repeat myself more than I can help, but it will do no harm to recapitulate; strong growth of new primary roots and of laterals on the existing primaries during the period from planting to winter; then winter dormancy; extended growth in spring of fibrous, feeding roots formed the previous autumn, and possibly some newly originating ones; strong growth of flowers and leaf in spring and summer. After harvest there will be vigorous development of new primary and feeding roots and of new daughter crowns.

This process will be repeated in the established plants throughout their productive life. There are certain to be some variations in the start of the different phases, according to soil and regional, or even localised, conditions, but the overall pattern is constant to the summer fruiting types.

We will now get right down to earth, and turn to severely practical matters. I hope that when dealing with these we shall see that some, at least, of the points already raised will have a definite bearing on such aspects as planting and soil management.

II

Soil and Compost

Our task is to keep as close to nature as gardening will allow. Wild strawberries at their best are unmistakably associated with moist, dark coloured, friable soil that smells of well rotted leaf mould. This has evolved from decomposed vegetation in the form of leaves, root fibres, decayed twigs and so on. Except for the root fibres, all the items that make up this rich compost have fallen on the surface, and have become gradually absorbed into it by the action of worms, rain, soil movement, oxygen, bacteria and the various other agents of natural composting. It is a process completely in the hands of nature, and provides a paramount lesson in strawberry growing.

The finest cultivated strawberries are not grown in soil that is deeply dug, where much of the relatively unfertile sub-soil may be mixed with the fertile top layer, or in extreme instances where the digger is inexperienced, may even replace it. In new gardens left in the state of dereliction that follows the bulldozer, top soil may have been entirely removed, in which case the surface and the regions below it will be low in fertility, and digging in the ordinary sense will do little more than open up the soil, thus improving drainage to some extent in heavy land, and improving conditions of aeration. Such improvement is essential, but by itself it will not do much to increase fertility.

We cannot emulate entirely the conditions of the thriving woodland plant, because these are the result of long periods of natural fertility, but we can do our best to achieve as near as possible the best alternative.

To do this we must first put into the plot something nearly approximating to the contents of the woodland soil. After that we must copy nature by feeding with organic matter from the top.

I want to emphasise this emulation of nature. We must build on a good foundation; where strawberries are concerned this means building on organic matter, a fact that can hardly be over-emphasised.

Organic matter, in gardening terms, spells correctly made compost. Those who are unfamiliar with compost making would do well to contact the Henry Doubleday Research Association, Bocking, Braintree, Essex, which is devoted to organic gardening and will offer reliable and extremely knowledgeable advice.

All I will do here is to sound a few warning notes, and try to give some idea of the functions of compost. It is rather unfortunate that standards vary from the excellent to the execrable. This has possibly come about as a result of the notion that all you have to do to make a compost heap is to chuck on it all the kitchen rubbish and just leave it to rot.

This leads not to decomposition, which is the essence of composting, but to putrefaction, which is rottenness or corruption, the antithesis of composting. It is absolutely no use at all hurling a load of slimey waste on to the soil. A good compost is almost eatable; it is a warm, friable, rich looking substance, slightly moist but never wet; it is dark brown, and capable both of absorbing rain without releasing excessive moisture through evaporation when the material is used as a surface mulch, and of retaining moisture when dug into the soil. In the former case it acts as a non return valve, in the latter as a leaven to consolidate a light and too freely drained soil, and to provide a moisture reserve. On heavy land it is an opening agent, making the soil lighter, improving aeration and drainage, and enabling water to 'spread' evenly through-out the root zone, so that the fine absorbing hairs can drink in comfort.

Think of it as a living and life giving substance, for this is what it is. It has been reduced from its original state of mixed vegetation to one of friability by the action of vast numbers of microscopic bacteria and other organisms which are themselves inhabitants of all healthy soil. These derive their energy from the nitrogen content of the rough material and in turn use that energy to break the material. They are the agents of fertility, feeding on fertility, producing fertility. When we dig such compost in we introduce a universe of life that enriches the soil and improves the root environment of our plants.

These conditions are utterly remote from the 'sourness' that is caused by excessive dressings of raw manure, or by waste matter which has not been composted but has merely gone rotten. Matter of this kind is virtually inert. If it is attended by any forms of life, these are likely to be merely certain fungi that fatten on rotting substances. The stuff will certainly break down in time, for in time everything breaks down, but the process will be a putrefying rather than a fertilising one.

By contrast, it is hardly possible to harm our strawberries with high grade compost, no matter what the soil type. In this respect it is worth noting that in certain realms of natural science, 'richness' is equated with pollution. The bed of a farmyard pond is a good example. This can become over enriched with animal urine and excreta to the point where the state existing is known as eutrophication. The same thing can occur in lakes fed by streams carrying fertilizer run-off via the land. Eutrophic waters are so enriched by chemical reaction, notably nitrification, that their whole environment becomes grossly upset, and species of highly undesirable fungi may smother the surface.

A somewhat comparable process, though with different results, occurs in soils over-enriched with manures of high nitrogen content. They become, for practical purposes, polluted. Good compost is not in the same category. It is not high in nitrogen, and in any case it is already reduced to a structure that does not impede drainage, or block air spaces in the soil. Neither chemically nor physically is it injurious.

My remarks about kitchen waste should not be taken to mean that it is unsuitable. On the contrary, it all helps, but it must be chopped up into reasonably small pieces. We do not want huge cabbage leaves, or gigantic discarded carrots and so forth. If these are slung on the heap in that state, as they so often are, they will not 'break down' but will simply go rotten.

Perhaps the final proof of a compost is its disappearance from the surface into the soil. If it does disappear after one growing season, we can be pretty certain it is good quality, of a consistency that ensures its incorporation into the soil. If it is still plainly visible on the surface, then it obviously is not of this standard, and so is not doing its job. Where it lies thickly it will impede rain, instead of allowing its entry. The soil will then be puddled on top and insufficiently wetted in the root area. The point on which we must be clear is that, although the end product of compost is fertility, the material does not directly feed the plants. Even in its perfected state, it is more of a soil conditioner and a substance for conserving moisture, than a plant food. But it will contain inherent nutritional properties that will finally benefit the plants.

SOIL TYPES

Most of us are stuck with our soil and must make the best of it. To do that we need to have some notion of how strawberry plants respond to varying soil types. Gardeners are not geologists and are content to divide soils into three main categories, light, medium and heavy. Apart from these, there is also chalk soil.

Light soil is loamy sand, normally brown or light brown, but often greyish or blackish in some heathland areas. With a relatively high content of coarse sand, ie some 40% of coarse particles of 2.0 to 0.2mm diameter, and a low one of clay, approximately 12% of particles of less than 0.002mm diameter, this soil in its ordinary state can be too hot, open and freely drained for strawberries.

Such land may be ideal for early root growth, since a sandy medium always encourages a strong initial root flush, but is far from ideal as a medium to sustain these roots and to encourage strong fresh ones. This means that after a good start, growth will fall off; although the cycle of root and top development will still occur, the progress within the cycle will not be maintained. But if we feed the soil liberally with organic matter before planting, and afterwards by mulching, we shall close up the excessive air spaces, cool the soil and provide a holding substance for water. Rain will then be available to the roots, instead of running away to the drainage zone or evaporating in the presence of too much soil oxygen.

Medium soil is sandy loam, with about 10% less of the sand particles mentioned above and 6% more of the clay, making it that much heavier. It is just about ideal for strawberries, but still needs compost on a maintenance basis to keep it ideal. It is distinguishable to the eye from the loamy sand by its darker colour; it feels heavier when rubbed in the hands, and there will be comparatively few sharp grains scratching the skin. This colour and rubbing test is anything but scientific, but it serves a good practical purpose, and enables even a beginner to get a useful idea of whether his soil is light or medium.

Heavy soils, though frequently thought of as clay, are more accurately described as silty and clay loams. (True clay is largely found in the sub-soil, except where bulldozers have gouged it out and pushed it on to the surface). Both are very close textured and under bad management can be fatal to strawberries. Aeration is often poor, a rising water table causes internal flooding, and rainwater floods the surface.

Silty loam is very low in coarse particles and high in fine; some 95% consists of particles of sand, silt and clay in the 0.2 to 0.002mm range, and only 5% of coarse sand, all of which adds up to a very finely knit soil. It is one in which organic matter plays a vital role. Without it, the crumb structure may break down; the silt and sand then separate. When conditions turn wet, the silt is caught up in water movements, and carried about in the soil. As the water drains away, pockets of

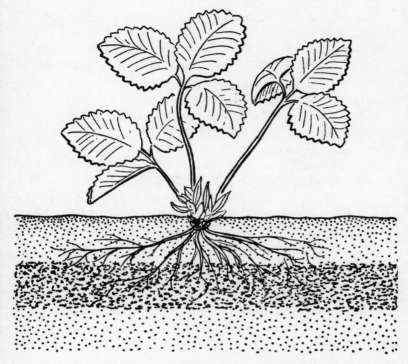

Section of hardpan, resisting roots

silt are left as deposits, and these set in hard layers. Many readers must be familiar with the sudden and unexpected resistance to the spade which turns out to be not a stone but a crust of 'sand'. This is in fact a crust of transported silt whose presence is the surest indication anyone could want that the soil is begging for humus.

Give it plenty of organic matter, and keep up supplies each year, and you will transform a potentially disastrous strawberry soil into a good one.

The clay loam does not separate, but under adverse conditions it binds when wet into a sticky, impenetrable state, becoming waterlogged and airless. When it dries out, it forms bone-hard clods that can break a spade, and a man's heart, if not his back.

Soil men recognise various sub-divisions of the gardener's simple category, but they need not concern us here, for we do not have to put our garden soil under a microscope. The principle we must have in mind is that organic matter is the foundation on which to build, but that it performs two distinct functions that seem direct opposites in print, but in fact serve the same end.

The functions seem opposed because one is the closing up of soil, the other the opening up. In both cases the object is to strike the right balance between excessive closeness and excessive openness. In the simplest terms we could say that the open soil is hot, the close one cold; what we seek is warmth, or the happy medium. With this goes the ideal root environment, because all the factors that add up to this combine to produce 'warmth', or fertility.

Chalk soils are highly alkaline, and the strawberry being by nature a plant of organically constituted soils, prefers some acidity, with a pH of about 5 to 6. Its usual reaction to chalk and limestone is to go down with lime induced chlorosis.

No cultivated chalk soil is pure chalk, but in many gardens on the great downland formation of southern England, or the limestone hills of the Cotswolds and Yorkshire, the surface soil is thin, and alkalinity lies only a few inches below. On such land we shall plant strawberries at our peril. Strange things happen daily, and we may succeed, but the odds on success are not great. If, however, there is chalk below the root depth of strawberries, say at 12in, but with a non-chalky top soil, there is no reason why strawberries should not do well.

Sometimes the top layer is directly derived from the underlying chalk. In this case much depends on the age of the formation, and the extent to which it has become mixed with transported soils down the ages. This in turn will depend in large measure on various factors, not the least of which is the way the land has been cropped in the past.

Page 35 Removing unwanted runners

Page 36 (left) Runners rooted in pots; *(right)* Royal Sovereign forced in greenhouse

If the root area is chalky, but mixed with darker soil, the pH will probably be somewhere within the plants' requirements, but still too high for success. In this event iron chelate could be used to offset the worst effects of alkalinity, but it is expensive, and where several applications were needed annually the cost would be too high for the returns, and it would be cheaper to visit the nearest greengrocer and buy strawberries.

Gardeners sometimes imagine they can lower the alkalinity of their soil by adding peat. This is a false notion; it would take years to achieve any significant lowering of the pH. The thing to do is to try to prevent the effects of lime induced deficiency, not to try to make the soil less limey.

Broadly speaking, the only other soils on which strawberries would probably fail are gravels and thin surface layers over rock. But with some labour and ingenuity even these can serve, though only as a base, and not as a root run.

A market gardening friend of mine overcame this very problem by planting on ridges of imported soil—a dodge which is also a good way of overcoming red core disease, as we shall see later. Importing does not mean getting in tons of soil at a ruinous cost from miles away. It can often be done by the simple procedure of removing the top soil from some spare corner and building it up with compost as necessary. By regularly adding compost mulches, the ridges can be developed into first class strawberry beds. If, say, three ridges can be established, they can be rotated every third year, with catch crops being sown in the intervening seasons. If they are kept about 18in high, the uncongenial base will never affect the strawberry roots. Very often the alleys between the ridges can be utilised for shallow rooting subjects, especially if the root run is kept friable with compost.

Having built his ridges, my friend uses nothing but compost for topping up. Soil is not needed. There is now, after some ten years, such a splendid physical condition from annual mulching of the original soil that practically anything will flourish. I must point out that he makes real compost.

C

There are various soil conditioners available that are reputed to transform intractable soils. Such materials have been going in some form or other for years, with varying degrees of success. One is now offered, based on gypsum, and containing certain plant nutrients. Gypsum is calcium sulphate and therefore a form of lime. This type of conditioner could prove useful on heavy loam, but should be avoided on chalky soils, since it would merely increase alkalinity.

DRAINAGE: WATER RETENTION

As far as moisture is concerned, the ideal soil is the one that retains a reserve of water during dry weather. There is the natural reserve in the form of a water table, whose level fluctuates according to the amount of rain reaching it. In drought the table falls to its minimum; in periods of heavy rain it rises to its maximum.

Below the point at which the table starts lies the underlying rock. This is not a solid bed, but is punctured by a vast maze of cracks and crannies. Through these runs the surplus rain water, eventually to pass away as drainage. This is known as ground water.

Before rain can reach this low level it has to moisten the outer surfaces of all the soil particles, while some is absorbed through plant roots. It will not move downwards until the particle moistening is complete.

Thus we see that the downward movement of water is a gradual one only; before any one layer can be reached, the one immediately above it must be wetted to 'field capacity', ie to the point at which the surfaces of all the soil particles in that layer are incapable of holding on to more water. The continuing rain then passes over them and reaches lower levels.

The same slow process occurs below the water table among the rock crannies. These crannies must be filled with water from above before the exit into the drainage zone can begin.

In times of heavy and prolonged rain the entire water table

zone may become saturated. When that happens the soil cannot accept any more water, and surface flooding occurs.

In times of prolonged drought the water table zone becomes almost completely dry; the spaces between the soil particles which ideally are filled with air and water, are then filled with air only, and in the absence of applied water to saturate the root zone to field capacity, the plants will wilt. And since they take up all their soil nutrients in solution, they will go not only thirsty, but hungry as well.

Even in drought periods, however, some moisture will remain in the lowest reaches of the water table, because it will be drawn up from the ground water by capillary attraction to fill what is known as the capillary fringe. But it will be far below the strawberry roots and therefore of no help to them.

What I have, for convenience, called the water table zone is more correctly known as the zone of aeration. It is the entire stratum from soil surface to water table, and its correct term implies the abiding necessity for a well structured, airy region, but one capable of retaining moisture in dry weather.

We must appreciate that this principle applies throughout the whole range of strawberry culture, whether we are growing on a field or garden scale or in a flowerpot. Certainly in the latter case we are not concerned with rock strata and ground water, but we are very definitely concerned with a root medium that is, in effect, a scaled down version of the garden plot.

We have just seen that when each layer is wetted to field capacity, further rain seeps through to wet the next layer. Now here is a point of fundamental importance in our consideration of soil texture. If the strawberry bed is composed of thick, lumpy rubbish that passes for compost, the downward passage of rain will be checked, and instead of having a zone that is thoroughly wetted but still capable of allowing rain to seep through to lower levels, we shall have patches in the soil that create miniature floods. This is most easily seen on hard packed surfaces, where depressions hold tiny ponds, or where, in the absence of depressions, water just lies on the surface, or runs off it where there is a slope.

These conditions in the root zone are fatal to strawberry roots. The absorbing hairs are lying in water, in places from which oxygen has been excluded, and they will become asphyxiated.

In any soil the zone of aeration obviously depends basically on soil depth. We have noted that 10-12in is about the limit of downward root growth for strawberries, and that the lowest region accommodates mainly scattered lengths of primaries and secondaries, usually with few absorbing roots. Nevertheless, we need a deeper zone than this.

A minimum ten inch depth of good drainage is classed as a very shallow soil. It tends to flood in wet weather and to dry out in times of drought. A minimum drainage of 15in is a shallow soil. It is the lowest limit for strawberries, but can be turned to good account on sandy loam and loams. An 18in

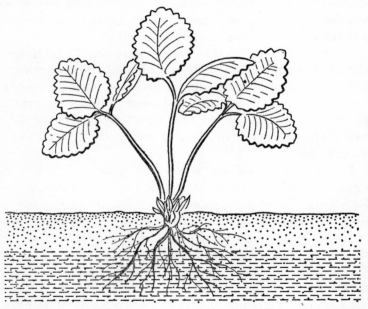

Water-logged sub-soil. Roots in this area will die

depth is moderately deep, and will be first rate for straw-berries. Anything deeper is, of course, admirable.

The simplest way of judging drainage depth is to dig out holes of 15in and 18in deep in autumn, and see whether they remain filled with water during winter. If the water disap-pears during the day, all is well. If it remains for long periods, that is a sure sign of impeded drainage. If it runs out as you watch it, this is an equally sure sign of too free drainage.

This test is of course done in periods of normal winter rainfall. Under flood conditions, where the whole area is saturated, it cannot apply.

Impeded drainage does not necessarily mean that straw-berries would be hopeless. Apart from ridge culture, much can often be done by laying drains to a soakaway, though this can be a laborious job, or by simply taking out drainage channels 18in to 2ft deep on an increasing gradient to a soak-away. They should have cinders, rubble and so on laid in the base to a depth of about 9in and then filled in. The soakaway should be some 3ft deep, and about 3 to 4ft square, and should be well packed with rubble.

It is useful to know the approximate amounts of water available to the roots per foot depth when the soil is wetted to field capacity. On loamy sands the figure is 0.7in. On sandy loams it is 1.6 to 1.8; on loams to silt loams, 2.5 to 3.2; on clay loams 1.5 to 2.0in. So yet again, the best textured loams score the most points.

In matters of soil improvement we must appreciate that we cannot change the basic character of the land, but we can still improve it where necessary. We cannot change a pre-dominantly clayey soil into a medium loam, but we can estab-lish conditions that simulate the loam, which is the next best thing.

The principle is that the heavier the soil, the lighter and 'longer' should be the type of material we dig in, and the lighter the soil, the heavier and 'shorter' should the stuff be. Long straw is the best thing of all for heavy land, but is virtu-ally out of reach of town gardeners. Hedge clippings make a good substitute, together with pea and bean haulms and all the cut down stems of woody plants gathered from autumn clearing. Never burn these if you garden on heavy land and want to grow strawberries. Dig them in, some laid 'long' in the trenches, others chopped up, scattered over the surface, and worked in as you dig. Wood ash certainly lightens heavy land, but much less benefit will be derived from burning the stalks and using the ash, than from using the stalks. What we need is bulk, not scattered ashes.

On lighter soils we want a binding material, and there is nothing better for rural gardeners than strawy stable manure, not fresh, and not stale stuff that has been left out in the open for years and has lost all its goodness, but which has been left for a month or two to mature. It can either be used as it is, or mixed with compost. Very often we can compromise; in this event, we can buy ready to use organic manures derived from seaweed, which are suitable for heavy and light land, though they may not open up the former as effectively as the previous materials mentioned.

III

Site

The choice of a site for strawberries is obviously limited in most gardens, but even so there are certain points to consider.

In rural gardens, frost damage to blossoms is an important thing to guard against. It is much less of a danger in built up areas, since there is always some degree of heat in the atmosphere of these.

Spring frosts are primarily radiation frosts. The daytime heat gathered by the flowers is radiated away into the air during clear, cloudless nights. On such nights winds at freezing point or below, known as Katabic winds may occur. They flow down from high to low ground, replacing the warmer air given off by all surfaces, including the strawberry flowers. Wherever their passage is checked, by a wall, a hedge or building, or by meeting high ground, they build in height and density, until the top of the layer overcomes the height of the obstruction, when flow is resumed, but leaving behind it the built up layer. An area that becomes filled with air in this way is known as a frost pocket. Blossoms surrounded by the air will be frosted.

Since strawberries are ground plants, it is easily seen that only a low layer of freezing air is necessary to envelope them.

In so far as a choice of site is possible, the following points should be considered. If the garden is on sloping ground, and particularly if at the bottom of the slope there is a barrier to air movement, plant at the top of the slope, or as near the top as you can. If the removal or the lessening of barriers at the foot of a slope is a feasible proposition, this should receive due thought. For example, a thick hedge bottom can hold up enough cold air to cause frost damage, but if it is thinned out the cold air will escape.

Amateurs sometimes have difficulty in recognising frost damage. The most susceptible stage is the open flower. Frost damaged flowers show 'black eyes', which denote death of the styles. Often the petals are unharmed, but as these play no part in the fertilization process, their escape is immaterial as far as this is concerned. Flowers which have shed petals are almost as susceptible, though it is more difficult in their case to diagnose frost damage, because the styles go dark naturally. But where damage has occurred the achenes will turn dark olive green. Even before this stage is reached, suspected frost damage can be checked for by cutting through a 'fruitlet', ie an undeveloped berry, to expose the seed bases. If these are discoloured, the reason is almost certainly frost.

Unopened flowers at the white bud stage are also very liable, but flowers still enclosed in the sepals are much less so.

Fruitlets are frequently killed, particularly when still carried on upright stalks; when they have made enough weight to bend the stalks over, so that the fruitlets are either sheltered by leaves or are close to the relatively warm soil, they will often escape, or will suffer only partial damage.

Fruit malformation may be caused by partial frost damage, when it is seen as 'bald' protuberances, either devoid of achenes or with one or two, usually aborted, on the surface. Malformation due to imperfect pollination may also take this form.

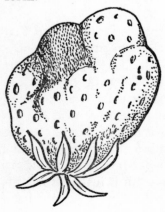

Frost damage during berry growth

The fact that fruitlets held close to the soil will suffer the least damage points to the wisdom of not strawing the beds down until the frost season has passed, normally after the third week of May. The soil does of course lose surface heat by radiation, but it also absorbs enough heat on a warm, cloudless spring day to enable some retention. This reservoir of heat is gradually lost during the night, as radiation proceeds, but strawberries near the soil surface are, in varying degrees, protected by a layer of warmth. But if straw is laid over the surface it will prevent the warm air escaping, and the fruitlets will then be much more liable to frost. If straw is laid before or during blossom, the possibility of frosted flowers will be increased.

The same thing applies to mulching, a matter we shall deal with in due course.

The danger of low lying sites is not confined to frost. There is the added danger of stagnant air. Just as cold air lies about in hollows, so does air movement in these tend to be restricted in certain circumstances. We all know the close, dank atmosphere of hemmed in places on days of high humidity or in periods of high temperature and drizzling rain. These conditions favour the rapid spread of such fungus troubles as grey-mould of the berries and various forms of leaf disease.

Free air circulation at ground level and just above is not an easy thing to provide for in a garden, but it is certainly an easy thing to obstruct. If we plant our strawberries in close association with such things as runner beans, artichokes, brussels sprouts, and similar high growing subjects, we are almost certain to create conditions leading to some degree of stagnation at strawberry level. But if we restrict surrounding plants as far as possible to low growing subjects, then at least we shall not be inviting trouble.

I once saw a perfect example of bad siting, where a gardener had planted strawberries between a block of artichokes about 6ft high and several rows of rampaging runner beans. To add to the trouble, the rows ran east to west, which meant that the strawberries were largely hidden from sunlight, being overshadowed by the artichokes. Things would not have been quite so bad if the rows had run north to south. There were periods of rain that spring, and the plants did not get enough sun to dry them out quickly, added to which air movement was much restricted. These conditions, combined with failure to spray against greymould, resulted in heavy attacks of this disease, and practically the entire crop was ruined.

It is well established that certain plants flourish in association, while others can create antagonistic effects. Cabbages, for example, are said to be antagonistic to strawberries. Dwarf beans, spinach, lettuce and borage are supposed to exert a good influence. This may sound far fetched, and some of the allegedly useful relationships seem to me to be based on folklore, but the concept of happy families in the plant world is fundamentally sound, and relates to such things as the interaction of root secretions and their complex effects on soil environment, soil pests and diseases.

PLANTING

The amount of preparation necessary will depend on the general state of the soil. If it is in good heart, little more than surface digging or forking over should be needed, but let us not shirk our duty if sterner measures are required. We will assume that these are required, and that we have to dig in a basic supply of compost.

Digging in implies putting the stuff into the root area of the strawberry plants, so that the roots can benefit from the fertility processes. This simply means half-trenching, or bastard trenching as it is quaintly called, to a depth of 10in, forking the compost into the bottom of each trench as we proceed. An initial trench is taken out, the soil heaved straight from spade into wheelbarrow. The load is then wheeled to the other end of the plot. Into this initial trench compost is forked. The base of the trench can first be forked if necessary, to break it up, but this should not need doing on loamy soil. The soil from the second trench is then turned into the first and the process repeated until the final trench is taken out. This is then filled with the soil from the wheelbarrow.

I have tried to make it sound painless, because I should hate to think of anyone getting the notion that it is hard labour, and deciding to do it in what they imagine to be the easy way by simply spreading compost and then turning this in with a spade.

My way in fact is painless, or nearly so; the other way may sound easier, but in practice it is virtually impossible to dig compost straight from the soil surface into the root run. Most of it just gets mixed up with surface soil and becomes a confounded nuisance when you start planting, and is of little value to the plant roots.

Half-trenching is *not* deep digging. Only the top soil is removed; on many soils, but certainly not on all, the trench bottom will mark the upper layer of sub-soil. This is not removed, but at most merely forked over to break it up.

It is always as well to have in mind the total compost needs for the plot. To work these out on a weight basis is a bit of a hit and miss method, since weights vary so much according to the type of compost, but we should aim for about a hundredweight, or one full barrowload, per 12sq yd, a barrowload being the amount contained in an old fashioned, man-sized wooden barrow, not one of those ridiculous metal toys which today are dignified by the name of wheelbarrow. These have perhaps half the capacity of the wooden type.

One hundredweight per 12sq yd is a lot of compost by garden standards, more than it may seem in print, and if the stuff is in short supply, as it usually is, it is far better to stick to this basic dressing and to be content with a smaller plot, rather than skimping things by spreading compost too thinly over a large area.

This applies particularly to light land—the greensands of Surrey and parts of Bedfordshire, for example, and any hot, gravelly soil where drainage is very free and drought is a danger.

Few gardeners could spare compost at more than the rate

of a full-sized barrowload per 12sq yd for any one crop, but if we are out to grow good strawberries, we should regard this amount as irreducible, unless we are lucky enough to be on really fertile land. On the assumption, admittedly not always valid, that land taken for building is not first class agriculturally, we can with fair safety reckon that strawberry plots in new gardens will need compost at the highest rate than can be spared.

In order to get a reasonably accurate idea of the amount of compost to put in the trenches, an initial area of 12sq yd should be marked off, to take the first barrowload. From then onwards it is easy to calculate the amount to put into each trench.

Where heavy land is concerned, 'long' material, ie hedge trimmings, bracken etc, together with sand and wood ash, will help to open up the soil, and may be mixed with compost.

Having dug in our compost during July for August planting, or in March for spring planting, the final steps are to firm the soil by treading the plot, and to rake over to ensure a level surface.

Spring planting is quite permissible, though any blossoms that appear must be removed, for we cannot expect plants set in spring to carry a crop in the same year. They will do so, to some extent, if the blossoms are left, but they will suffer for it later.

We could easily dismiss planting by saying, 'Buy your plants in Jiffy pots and insert pots with their tops level with the soil surface, or root your runners in these pots and plant likewise'. Those who are content with the barest necessary information can skip the rest of this section, but those who want to know something about the effects on strawberry roots of shallow, deep, and normal planting should read on. Shallow planting means that the entire crown is above soil level; deep planting means just deep enough for the soil to cover the crown completely; normal planting is when soil level is about mid-way up the crown.

Deep planting, though not ideal, does not generally have

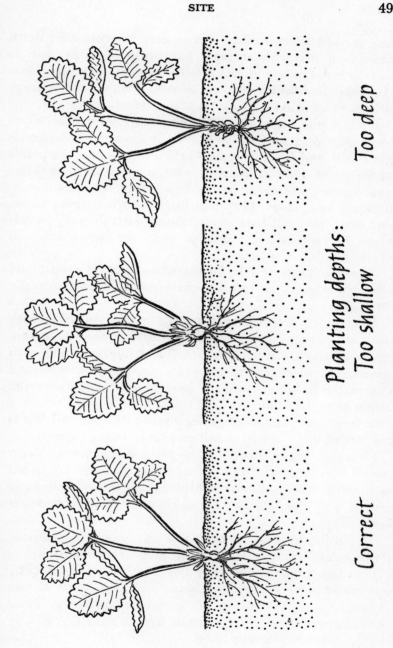

Planting depths:
Too shallow

Too deep

Correct

any marked adverse effect. There may be more root death than with normal planting, and growth of main roots is usually less, but lateral root growth does not appear to suffer. At twelve months from planting, overall vigour can be more or less the same as for plants set at the normal depth.

Shallow planting gives a different picture. At first, all seems well. New primary roots are fewer in number, but laterals grow well, and at six or seven weeks after planting the plants appear to be doing satisfactorily. A few weeks later, however, new primary roots may be about a month behind those on normally set plants. They will carry relatively few laterals, and many may not have made contact with the soil. In this event they will be red at the tips, and a number, possibly all of them, will have died.

The net result will be plants whose general vigour and cropping capacity are inferior when compared with normally set ones.

Now it is all very well to talk about 'normal' planting, with the soil halfway up the crown. It is fine in theory, but not always easy to achieve in practice. But shallow planting, with the crown clear of the soil and swinging about it easy enough to visualise in both theory and practice, and is therefore the easiest thing to avoid.

So long as the crown is making contact with the soil, but is not buried, the planting depth may be reckoned correct.

Firm planting is essential. Each plant should resist a sharp tug; if it comes out, you can be certain that the soil is not nearly firm enough. Roots are stimulated into growth by close contact with the soil, but are discouraged where contact is loose.

The soil must of course be friable and reasonably moist. If it is wet and sticky, wait until conditions have improved.

Root trimming was once an act of faith, done religiously by every head gardener. It does stimulate an initial flush of new shoots, but on balance does not increase plant vigour. It is, however, useful where necessary to prevent bunching of very long roots in the planting holes.

Professional growers often plant with a dibber. The hole is made, the plant inserted, and the soil firmed by pushing the dibber in close to the roots and levering it towards the plant. There is a knack in this that comes only by practice, and in any case the action does not firm a loose soil very well. The best tool for amateurs is a trowel. The hole is taken out, the roots placed in position, and enough soil to cover them is spooned back. Next, this soil is firmed by ramming it with the trowel handle, taking care not to break off any roots. Root breakage will not occur if enough soil to act as a padding is first returned. Finally, the hole is topped up to the correct level.

The layout of the bed should ensure that one can move about without trampling all over the plants. It should not be necessary, for example, to walk on the bed for fruit picking. If no more than four rows at 30in apart are set in any one block, with a clear pathway dividing the blocks, it will be a simple matter to restrict our walking to the pathways and to pick two rows from each side of the block. Fifteen inches between plants is about the minimum; 18in is better for the modern vigorous varieties.

The plants can of course be set at 15 × 15in, or 18 × 18in if no runner production is contemplated, but if home propagation is wanted, then the 30in spacing between the rows will allow room for runner growth (*see page 35*).

IV

Weed Control

A basic need of general maintenance is to ensure that the plot is free of perennial weeds, especially couch grass, ground elder, bindweed, creeping buttercup and nettles.

The great majority of garden strawberry plots are quite small, which means that the removal of underground weed roots is relatively easy when we are digging the soil to prepare the bed. These roots *must* be pulled up, and this includes broken scraps.

If the bed is clean to start with all that we need worry about is the suppression of annual weeds, plus the pulling up of any perennials that do occur. The former can be ensured to a marked extent merely by mulching, or routine strawing, but the application of simazine to prevent germination may be called for. We should realise that, apart from the competition for soil moisture which even annual weeds can cause, they are also sources of greymould infection. In fact much of this extremely destructive berry disease originates on weeds, so for this reason alone, weed control is important.

Although simazine is safe on strawberries when correctly used, its misuse will almost certainly cause damage. Makers' instructions must be strictly followed; spray only at recommended times, and never use more than the stated mixture.

The best thing I can do here, by way of general survey, is to draw on the information of the Ministry of Agriculture. Simazine is applied to clean land to control germinating weed seeds or very young weeds. The soil should be moist at the time of application. Freshly planted runners are liable to injury, but dipping their roots in activated charcoal may reduce injury. (Experimental work has shown that runners treated thus have not been injured by normal simazine rates one week

Page 53 Strawberries flowering under cloches

Page 54 Strawberries under polythene tunnels; tunnels rolled up for ventilation

after planting.) Runners planted in late summer or early autumn, but not dipped, have been successfully treated with simazine later in the same season when well established, but a warning note from a different source states that runners (not dipped) should not be sprayed for at least six months after spring planting, or for nine months after autumn planting.

Such conflicting advice is unfortunate, and may possibly be based on differing conditions of soil and plant vigour. The safest assumption is that simazine should be withheld from newly planted runner beds when the young plants are obviously not making good headway.

The use of steam activated charcoal would normally be confined among amateurs to horticultural clubs, allotment holders and the like, since it is not usually sold in lots of less than a hundredweight, costing about £20. It is a lot of money, but clubs with enough cash in the kitty and enough strawberry growers to make the purchase worthwhile, would find the charcoal a good investment if their strawberry growing members were sufficiently simazine minded.

The Ministry says that on established beds simazine may be used between July and December to give weed control through winter into spring.

At the Efford Experimental Station in Hampshire, damage from applying simazine to newly planted runners was greater the shorter the interval between planting and spraying, and in the Midlands was more serious with August planted than with September planted runners.

The protective value of the root dip has been established in Scotland and Northern Ireland, and charcoal in the steam-activated form was the most suitable. Root dipping is more effective than placing charcoal round each runner at planting time.

Once the plants are well established, spraying between late summer and December has generally been safe and efficient, but yields were reduced in one experiment when spraying in December, probably owing to a long cold winter that caused the herbicide to remain unchanged in the soil until spring.

D

Spring applications may cause variable damage according to the degree of dormancy of the plants. Reports from Northern Ireland state that susceptibility of the crop increases gradually from January to April. In Jersey simazine has been successfully used in January. In Scotland it is recommended for use on established plants in late February or early March. In the Midlands it was used before cloching the plants in March without causing damage.

Used in March at the Stockbridge House Experimental Station in Yorkshire, and at the Luddington ES in Warwickshire, simazine reduced yields, and in the Midlands severe injury was caused by April applications.

In Scotland a spray is recommended on maiden plants when 3–4 fully expanded leaves have been produced, ie in May or June. This may cause some initial leaf yellowing, but the plants should outgrow this in 2–3 weeks.

The variety Cambridge Favourite was found more sensitive than others at Efford, but most varieties other than the continental ones are relatively resistant to damage from correct dosages. This does not necessarily mean that the latter are susceptible; some are, however, known to be so in certain circumstances, especially Regina.

It should not be assumed that all annual weeds are killed by simazine; some that are resistant are knotgrass, *Polygonum aviculare*, various species of Anthemis—mayweed, corn chamomile etc, and groundsel, *Senecio vulgaris*.

Readers will appreciate that when they buy a tin of simazine from the garden shop, the label will contain information and advice of a general nature only. It is obviously beyond the scope of manufacturers to include detailed data based on regional experience from experimental work. Thus if damage does occur from time to time in spite of rigid adherence to makers' instructions, the material cannot really be blamed. The causes are more likely to be related to local conditions of soil and climate and the condition of the plants.

I hope that the information I have culled from regional sources will provide background help in the use of this herbicide. It should be recognised that when we talk of spraying the runners of the plants, this means spraying the weedy soil in which the plants are growing. I would reiterate the need for damp soil; spraying when the ground is dry is useless.

If it should become necessary to burn out weeds between the rows, paraquat could be used to kill annuals and the leaves of perennials, though as it will not kill roots, it will not give more than temporary control of perennials. It is fatal to strawberry leaves, especially on young plants, which means that in this case extreme care must be taken to ensure that no drift occurs, and that only the weeds receive the spray. This can be done by applying the spray in large droplets that will not drift, eg with a water can fitted with a rose having large holes. Obviously it cannot be used in runner beds.

I include this information for the benefit of those who feel they must use weedkillers, not because I think such methods are desirable or even necessary. My view is that in the vast majority of gardens hand weeding is much to be preferred. But where this is done it is imperative to weed regularly, before the weeds have become established. There are two reasons for this. One is that the greater the leaf area of weeds, the greater the possible source of greymould; the other is that weeds must drink, and even annuals can take soil moisture that should go to the strawberries. A strong cover of annuals will absorb appreciable quantities of water, sometimes enough to cause the strawberry plants distress.

WATERING

With watering we come to something which may be thought of as a job to keep little Willie out of mischief. 'Go and water the strawberries, dear,' as mother might say persuasively and in suppressed desperation, as she grips the kitchen sink to stop herself from screaming. At which, little Willie, if he is at all co-operative, which is unlikely, will drift out to the strawberry bed, slosh about with a water can, or direct a jet from the hose at everything except the strawberries.

Mother bless her, will have earned a very brief respite, and Willie's watering will, to that extent, have fulfilled a noble cause, but the strawberries will not have noticeably gained.

The important point is that if the soil is in good fettle and is conserving moisture on which the plants can draw freely, then watering becomes largely a matter not so much of topping up as providing definite amounts at definite periods to serve a definite purpose. The threefold use of that word will, I hope, suggest that the subject of watering is one demanding certain emphasis.

There is good evidence to show that heavy watering at the wrong time can reduce crops. We have seen how flower initiation occurs mainly in late summer. If water is applied heavily immediately before this process starts it will delay flower development and reduce the number of flowers for the following year. If it is applied during the harvest period it may increase the size of the later picked fruits but will be unlikely to increase the following season's yields, because of the depressing effect it will have on flower bud differentiation. It is interesting to note that in German trials where water was withheld from a fortnight before harvest until September, differentiation was satisfactory, and a good watering after September increased the fruit crop the following year.

The greatest depressing effect on the next year's crop resulted from watering in August, after which a 25% crop reduction was recorded. Watering in June gave a 12% reduction.

To change from the negative to the positive, fruit number the following season was increased by irrigation in April by 13%, in September by 15%, and in October by 36%.

High moisture levels in the soil were therefore seen to depress flower bud differentiation, but to benefit the development of flower buds that had already been initiated. The largest number in the latter category occurred in October, when watering had the greatest effect on the following year's crop.

This is rather a far cry from little Willie's efforts, and illustrates our 'definite period' and our 'definite purpose'. Not every purpose is yet served, however, and we still have the amounts of water to consider.

I have just said that water applied during the harvest period is not likely to increase the following season's yield, and the implication is that this is because flower growth is checked. (The measure of increase in yield in experimental work may be defined as the extra crop obtained from some beneficial technique when compared with the yield obtained in the absence of that technique.) The best time to apply water to strawberries in general terms under British conditions is when the berries are ripening, but if the September–October period is dry, water applied then can improve the future cropping power of the plants.

The latter method ties up with German experiments, assuming that the soil at the time these were done was dry, though information on this point is sparse.

Naturally, if plants are at their highest state of performance, both in terms of current season's production and of flower bud formation for the next year's crop, we cannot boost them beyond this state. If this condition has obtained during the current season's cropping period, and continues in September–October, and if the soil is sufficiently moist in autumn, then watering will serve no good purpose.

But watering at the ripening stage will swell the berries and so improve total crop weight. Watering when strawing down has also had this effect. At this stage the berries are not actually ripening, but are swelling.

Mr J. E. Goode of the East Malling Research Station, who has made detailed studies of water needs, recommends a rate of $\frac{1}{2}$–1in of water applied to a width of 9in on each side of the row when berries are ripening. One inch of water is $4\frac{1}{2}$gal per sq yd.

It is quite commonly believed that once we start watering we have got to continue, and because of this belief gardeners often withhold water in the hopes that rain will fall and do the job for them. The idea that watering has to be continued is quite wrong provided the single application at the right time is adequate. This is the whole secret of achieving satisfactory results. It is useless to dribble about with a water can just moistening the surface. Remember what we said about the downward movement of water, how each layer of soil must be thoroughly wetted before any water can go deeper. Try sprinkling water over a patch of dry soil, and see the results. Only the surface will be moist. Immediately below, the soil will still be dry. We can sprinkle like this every day for days on end, without doing a scrap of good. The water never reaches the roots, and is simply wasted. But if the root area is saturated from one application, no more water will be needed unless there is a long period of drought.

The need for constant watering is always reduced, or eliminated, by the conserving properties of a mulch. Routine strawing down can fulfil these, a measure we will now consider.

STRAWING DOWN

The main object of strawing down is to keep the berries free of the soil surface. This prevents dirt and splashing from rain, and to some extent may reduce slug damage, and also greymould as a result of berry contact with wet earth. Straw also gets wet, but if it is laid lightly and not in great wodges, the rain will run through it, and the surface area will dry fairly quickly.

Straw is hard to come by even in many rural areas, and almost unobtainable for town gardeners, so we shall have to consider other methods as well. But where it can be obtained it is still the best material, because it acts as a true mulch, which the manufactured materials do not, in spite of their often being called mulches.

The dual purpose of protecting the berries and of acting as a mulch is always the one to have in mind. I do not myself greatly favour materials which absorb and hold rain, as distinct from letting it get through to the soil. Such materials also have the effect of impeding aeration of the soil, since they may form a closely compacted layer when they become wet.

Some people advocate sawdust. I do not like it much. If it is to be effective in protecting the berries it usually has to be so thick that it will form this undesirable layer. If it is laid thinly so as not to impede rain, it will not protect the berries very well. Also, the berries can collect fragments, and nobody picking a berry or two straight from the plants wants to eat sawdust.

Peat is quite good, though again not ideal in my opinion. This too absorbs moisture, and can become so wet that rain is held up on the surface and may even form puddles. It has virtually no direct food value, a point not appreciated by gardeners who shovel loads of peat round starving plants. Pine and spruce needles I have always found very good, though again not as a feed, but not everyone lives near pine trees.

Compost is probably as good as anything; it fulfils the protective function as well as straw does, provided it is clean, and it automatically breaks down and goes into the soil later in the season, whereas straw must either be burnt off—a hideous waste—or else carted off for compost. It will not have broken down much by the season's end, and if it is left it will tend to delay soil warming in spring.

Except with straw, the possibility of fragments adhering to the lowest berries always arises in the presence of organic mulches, but if the berries are picked with a length of stalk they can be washed lightly under the tap. Berries should always be picked by the stalk, in any event.

The dual use of compost fits in nicely with the need to delay berry protection until the danger of spring frost is over, together with the need to conserve spring and early summer moisture. As a general guide, the beginning of the third week in May is the time to straw down in the south and the midlands, and late May further north.

Manufactured 'mulches' are mainly in the form of black plastic strips that are laid along the rows and kept in position either by stones, or by turning their edges in under the soil.

They suppress weeds, and being black, attract the sun's rays, which are two useful functions, but why they should ever have been called mulches I do not know. Obviously they cannot let rain through, and to this extent may actually be harmful in drought periods. They can, however, increase yields and induce earliness, though results have proved variable, and no definite recommendations can be made. At Efford no increase or earliness resulted from their use in a wet season. In Cornwall benefit was seen in only one year out of two, increase from clothed plants being greater with autumn than with spring mulching.

Finally, there are fruit mats, which are usually raffia type squares, or oblongs, with a hole in the middle. The berries and leaves are gathered loosely and drawn through the hole, and the mat is bedded down on the soil surface. As a protective measure, these are good, but again they tend to hold up rain, though one particular make woven from palm leaves is said not to do this.

DEFOLIATION

Once the straw, or mulch, is laid, there should be little to do, outside pest and disease control, until harvest, other than watering and the pulling out of any perennial weeds that happen to crop up. After harvest comes the question of what to do with the straw, if this was used. Other forms of mulch, except compost, will of course be removed.

Soon after the last war it was found at East Malling, and perhaps earlier in Scotland, that defoliation after harvest can have beneficial results. The reason is that the old leaves produce a substance that inhibits blossom initiation. Not all varieties react similarly, however, and at the time of writing many new varieties are undergoing defoliation trials. However, there are useful data for a number of established varieties.

At East Malling two-year plants of Talisman defoliated after harvest increased their following year's crop by 119%; Cambridge Rival increased by 85%, and Cambridge Vigour by 41%. Redgauntlet and Merton Princess increased by 27 and 25% respectively, while on Cambridge Favourite the second year's crop was *decreased* by 11%.

The latest trials at Efford in Hampshire suggested that the autumn crop of Redgauntlet, a variety that often crops twice annually, is likely to be heaviest if no mowing is done after the summer harvest. If, however, it is decided to mow off to get rid of pests or diseases, the job must be done immediately the summer crop is off, if the heaviest possible autumn yield is to be had. The best combination appeared to be no mowing plus cloching in early September. The placing of cloches over the plants before this date, whether plants were mown or not, following the summer crop, reduced the condition and size of the berries. A possible explanation was that early cloching provided too high a temperature for the setting of the early flowers.

It should be appreciated that the normally damper conditions of autumn are favourable to slugs and snails. Control of these is essential, not only for autumn crops of Redgauntlet, but for all varieties that continue fruiting into autumn.

In the trial mentioned here, the summer crop was grown under cloches, and its final pick was on June 25th.

Defoliation can be done by simply cutting off the old leaves, or by burning off straw and leaves together. The second method as a means of pest control may be too drastic on Redgauntlet, inasmuch as it may put paid to an autumn crop, but it works well on other varieties, especially Sovereign. But as I have already intimated, it is wasteful, and many gardeners may prefer to fork off the straw and compost it. Another point is that although it destroys a number of soil pests, it must destroy harmless or possibly beneficial species as well. Some people make a good job of mowing off the leaves with a rotary grass cutter.

But where Sovereign is concerned, there is no doubt in my mind that it does a power of good to the plants. When I grew this variety commercially I burnt off regularly every year (I was lucky with my straw supplies). At first the bed looks a horrifying site. There is nothing but crowns and a few small leaves. But within a week or two new leaves will appear, and by autumn there should be a fine growth of fresh looking foliage.

The straw must never be allowed to burn fiercely round the plants. Choose a day when there is a fair breeze; light up-wind if the wind blows along the rows, and tease the straw about the plants with a fork just long enough to allow the flames to burn off the leaves. Never let the crowns become burnt.

Two rows at a time are ample. Often one row is enough. If you are burning off large beds and the fire gets out of control you will be rushing about like someone demented, bashing out the flames. As soon as you bash out one area, another will spring up. I know, for I once nearly lost control of several rows on an acre of plants separated from a fifty acre cornfield by only a footpath, and the wind was blowing right across the strawberry field and over the corn. That was twenty years ago, but I dream about it still.

One of the good effects of burning off is that it effectively removes diseased foliage. Fire is the ultimate purifier. On small beds where leaves can be cut off, it is sound policy to gather them up as one goes, and to burn them or bury them in the compost heap.

It might be mentioned in passing that although leaves carrying the common strawberry diseases are safely out of harm's way if buried in compost, the idea of introducing any disease to the compost heap is not a good one. The bonfire is the best place.

PART II

V

Container Growing

Container growing is the name given by nurserymen to plants grown in composition type pots and sent out complete in these, but it also has wider meanings. Wherever plants are set in a container, eg tub, window box etc, whether in the pots in which they came, or as runners dug out of the ground, they may be said to be container grown. The plants are grown by the nurseryman in high grade compost, such as Levington or John Innes, being rooted into this medium in the runner beds. The compost remains suitable throughout the life of the plants, and as the pots gradually break down during their time in permanent quarters, there is no pot-binding effect, and the roots are able to grow out into the surrounding soil. The great advantage is that there is no root disturbance when lifting.

All that the gardener need do is to ensure that the soil in which the potted plants are set is adequately drained and of good quality, and that the container allows an overall root depth of 10in. The container must have drainage holes in its base, covered with crocks to prevent blockage.

There cannot be any question of runner production for propagation, since there is no room for this, and runners must be cut off regularly, except where certain varieties that fruit on current season's runners as well as on the main plant are concerned. These are very ornamental as well as being productive, and are ideal for hanging baskets, window boxes and for any position where trailing plants would decorate.

As I mentioned in the introduction, there are various containers that ingenuity can devise. (I mention it again, for the benefit of those who never read introductions.) An old wheelbarrow, drilled in the base with about half a dozen drainage holes, and furbished on the outside as fancy dictates, often with paint, makes a first class home for strawberries. A hollow tree trunk fitted with a wire basket is another possibility, while tubs and water butts are excellent.

A standard 40gal water butt will take twenty four plants. Three rows of six holes to a row are bored, each hole being about 3in diameter. Normally, a water butt is hooped with two rings at the top and two at the bottom. Between each pair of hoops six holes are bored at equal distances, so that top and bottom holes line up vertically. Then a third row of six holes is bored round the centre, these being staggered between the top and bottom. Six 1in holes are bored in the base for drainage, and the barrel is stood on bricks. Lay 6in of drainage rubble on the base. Place a 6in drainpipe vertically in the centre of the barrel, get someone to hold it, and then fill it up with sand and small rubble. Fill up with soil to the first row of holes, firm it well, then from the inside push the plant crowns and foliage carefully through the holes. Firm the soil round the roots, and continue the process, lifting up the drainpipe gradually to leave a cylinder of drainage material behind. The circular space above the top row will take another six plants.

I do not know whether Raymond Bush was the originator of this method, but he certainly did publicise it.

This is a very good way of intensive strawberry growing, but it cannot be too strongly emphasised that its success depends upon a really good soil consistency. Again we come back to the question of water percolation. Water has a long way to go to reach the bottom row. Remember that it will not get there until the higher layers are thoroughly wetted. We are growing strawberries in a barrel, not a field, but we still have to wet the soil to field capacity. Remember the drainage into the ground water below the water table, and the zone of aeration that must be a zone of air and moisture. If soil consistency is too heavy, our efforts to wet the entire volume will almost certainly cause flooding, with water lying in the soil where air ought to be.

We see now that what was said earlier was not of merely academic interest, or mere padding to make up a number of words the publisher expects, but that it has a definite bearing on barrel cultivation, unlikely though it may seem. We have no ground water in our barrel and no water table, but we do have what is, in effect, a zone of aeration. We also have a modified form of ground water, this being the water that will trickle out of the drainage holes in the barrel base, to tell us that the entire zone of aeration is wetted to field capacity, and that no more water is needed.

When we are planting, we can ensure that the plants will have immediate moisture by watering each row as we proceed.

It is unlikely that we shall use an expensive compost for the rooting medium, so the best mixture is equal parts of good loam and our own skilfully made compost, plus a spadeful of sharp sand and a half dozen handfuls (or handsful) of bone meal to each barrowload of mixture. To get the equal parts, a bucket will come in handy.

This basic compound can be used for all forms of container growing if desired, but the standard rooting mediums are probably better for small containers.

Barrel cultivation does not allow growth to proceed in the way we discussed earlier, or at least it prohibits it in some measure, because growing space for crowns is largely confined to the holes. Thus we cannot expect the same crop weights that we could get from garden cultivation, but at least we have a lot of plants in a small area (*see page 18*).

I have seen some first rate examples of strawberries in country gardens grown in old stone troughs, and indeed have grown them this way myself. The mellow stone makes a perfect background to the foliage and fruit, and many of these ancient troughs have most pleasing shapes. They can often be picked up in provincial junk shops and yards, though picked up is hardly the phrase, since some of them are pretty weighty and need a trailer for transport. Also, as they are now becoming fashionable they are no longer going for a song.

They should be stood on stones or bricks, or stone ridge tiles of the same material, the latter blending best of all.

Ordinary window boxes are also suitable, and can provide a strawberry 'plot' for those who have no garden space. Earthenware bowls of the bulb growing type will each take one good sized plant, and are just the thing for providing a feast of strawberries for a special occasion, or for proving that anybody, no matter how limited the garden space, can have home grown strawberries.

One enterprising little girl I know has given her totty pot a new and unfamiliar existence by growing strawberries in it, after her father had made a few drainage holes in its base. She evidently does not believe in built in obsolescence; that child will one day go far.

It is worth mentioning here that strawberry growing is a splendid diversion for children; to grow something that is beautiful and that you can eat should keep a child employed usefully and in happy anticipation, and may even point the way to a life in horticulture, a profession which will seldom build a fat bank balance, but will bring riches of another kind.

PROPAGATION

Modern strawberry plants are not cheap, and although nurserymen naturally like us to scrap the fruiting plants after two, or at most three years of cropping, and to buy new stock, we may not all be able to afford the outlay. There is little doubt that regular replacement is the ideal, sometimes after only one year's crop, but apart from questions of finance, there is great satisfaction in raising one's own plants. But there is no satisfaction whatever in raising runners from diseased or poorly performing parents, and if we have any suspicion, or know for certainty, that our plants are infected with virus, we should never propagate from them.

Whatever the source of new plants, a rotational system of planting is essential. For this reason it is very unwise to set

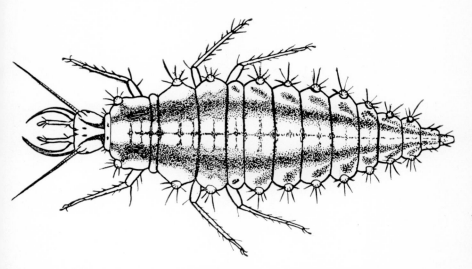

Page 71 *(above)* Larva of Green Lacewing, *Chrysopa carnea*, × 14; *(below)* strawberry seed beetle damage

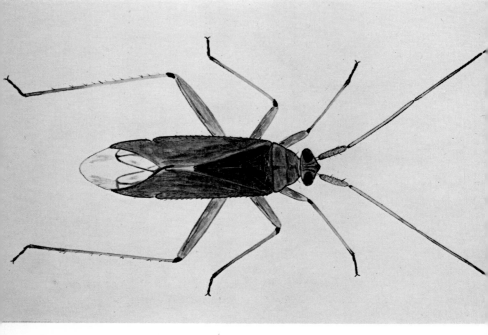

Page 72   (above) Black-kneed Capsid Bug, *Blepharidopterus angulatus*, ×14; (below) Tarsonemid Mite damage

aside a permanent strawberry plot in a fruit cage among long lived fruit subjects whose presence allows no facilities for rotation. The vegetable garden, which is rotated automatically, is the best place, but as far as possible we should avoid following potatoes and outdoor tomatoes with strawberries, because of the danger of verticillium wilt, a soil borne disease common to all three.

Generally, it is bad policy to propagate early in their life from plants whose main function is to produce fruit, since we need to conserve all the plant's energy for cropping. This of course is why runners are nipped off plants in the early fruiting days (*see page 35*). The two can, certainly, go together if parent plants are strong and in good production, but I prefer to defer propagation until the second cropping year.

The old method used to be to peg the runners down, or hold them down with stones, when they rooted into the bed. Rooting into pots in Levington or John Innes rooting compost is much better. The pots are sunk into the ground with their rims level with the surface, or are simply stood on the surface, and the young runner plants are pegged into them (*see page 36*). They must be pegged firmly enough to ensure that the young roots will contact the soil immediately they start to grow. Wire gardening pegs are the best things to use. Stones are really the lazy way, and the trouble with them is that they sometimes exert pressure at the wrong point, that is just behind the root, so that the young plant is not pressed to the soil, but is held clear of it. If this happens, little or no root progress will occur.

I am not very fond of allowing the runners to keep on growing, to give a chain of three or four plants all emanating from a single runner. Some people maintain that all the young plants on each runner are comparable in strength, and these conditions probably do arise sometimes, but my own policy is to allow no more than about four or five runners per parent plant, and no more than one young plant per runner. This gives four or five young plants from each parent and should satisfy most needs.

E

Any runners that grow on from the rooting plants are cut off just beyond their points of origin. Limitation of runners is not necessary where propagation from non-fruiting plants is the specific aim, but this is nurseryman's work and does not apply to the garden.

We saw that fruiting plants need watering at certain periods. The same applies to runner production. July and August are the vital months, and since this is the wrong period for watering fruiting plants, we must be careful to confine watering to the young ones as far as possible, more especially if propagation is undertaken early in the life of the parents.

When we come to transplant, which will normally be 4–5 weeks after pegging down, we simply cut the runners off and lift out the pots. If the latter are the composition type, they are buried as before in the planting bed. If they are clay pots, the plants complete with soil are tapped out by inverting the pots and knocking their rims smartly on a bench edge. The plants complete with soil are then planted with the top of the soil mould level with the garden soil. If the compost is good, and watering has been properly done, the root ball will come out cleanly from each pot.

If no pots were used, dig up the plants with a trowel, retaining a good mass of root soil. With all systems, planting must be done immediately. Do not lift the plants and leave them lying about.

We must always bear in mind the earlier mentioned 'branch' nature of the stolon. This is best regarded as a feeding channel from parent to offspring. The runner plant is drawing sustenance from the parent until such time as rooting is established. Thus although we want to transplant early, if a first year's crop is wanted, we must not sever the feeding channel until the young plant can dispense with parental aid. As I mentioned before, root establishment rather than obvious crown growth is the criterion, but the former will always be reflected in good leaf growth. Thus our transplanting date should be determined basically by leaf progress, though not necessarily by crown growth. Leaf establishment should be adequate within the four to five week period.

An alternative to cropping the first year after planting is to de-blossom the young plants in the spring after August planting, in order to encourage really strong and heavily cropping plants in the second year. This is almost essential with September set plants and even with August set plants of Royal Sovereign it can certainly be a good method. It does of course mean that if continuity of crop is to be assured, propagation must be done early enough in the life of the parent plants to allow these a cropping season while the young plants are building up. The fact remains, however, that first-year cropping from August set plants is perfectly acceptable with all varieties with the possible exception of Sovereign.

FORCING

Forcing is a means of advancing the picking date, sometimes by as much as three weeks, or considerably more where heat is used. It is also invaluable for anyone with an eye to a little pin money or who wants a hobby in retirement to supplement the pension. Early berries always make the best price and the cost of producing them on a hobby scale is quite small.

Many gardeners now have heated greenhouses, so we will consider these first.

Runners are rooted into 3in pots as previously described, and when good growth is established they are severed from the parents, and lifted complete in the pots. They are then transferred, complete with soil to 6–10in fruiting pots and placed in an ash bed in full sun, and kept watered sufficiently to ensure that they never dry out. The space in the larger pots is filled with standard potting compost.

An alternative method, to save transplanting, is to root the runners straight into fruiting size pots.

The potted plants are laid on their sides in late November, after a final watering to saturate the soil. Laying them on their sides is an insurance against soil stagnation. A covering of straw to prevent the soil moisture from freezing in hard weather is generally advocated.

Early in January the plants are placed on southerly shelves in the greenhouse, and watered if dry. No day heat should be given at this time; a month or so without it is required, until growth is under way, but full use should be made of what ever sun heat there is by good ventilation on sunny days.

Low night heat is, however, beneficial, a temperature of 40–45°F throughout January being advisable. Any signs of soil stagnation on the surface should be removed, and if necessary pots should be topped up with fresh material.

At this stage watering must be sparse, but it pays to damp the house down from time to time to prevent too dry an atmosphere. In February flower trusses should start to show. This is the time to raise night temperature to 50°F and to maintain this value during the days and to syringe the plants daily. Good ventilation is necessary, but draughts must be avoided. By mid-March full flower should be evident, and hand pollination with a soft brush is probably essential, since there is seldom the same amount of insect activity inside a greenhouse as outside, at least in mid-March. We will deal with the whys and wherefores of pollination and fertilisation in due course; here, the mechanics will suffice.

Pollen is transferred from anthers to stigmas when the former have split to release the pollen and when the latter are sticky and receptive. Pollen must be dry, which means that no syringing must be done during the pollination period. All that is necessary is to dab the flowers once a day, about noon, with the brush. Pollen is always more viable when it first appears, which means that dabbing is best done systematically as the anthers open and pollen is revealed. The longer the grains remain on the anthers the less likely are they to effect pollination.

The largest possible fruits are obtained by early thinning, ie at petal fall, to leave about ten berries per plant, but this is obviously a matter of choice.

A moist atmosphere, with the plants syringed several times

daily in sunny weather, and good watering to swell the berries, is the programme, with a night and day temperature of 55°F. Overhead ventilation during the day is needed, but the house should be closed early in the evenings.

To prevent the berries from contact with the soil, forked sticks are useful, though some varieties hang over the pot edges, clean of soil. When ripening starts, temperature is lowered by between 5 and 10°, and free ventilation is allowed by day, and overhead by night (*see page 36*). If the earlier forcing conditions are maintained, fruit flavour will suffer. Syringing should be stopped once ripening starts, but damping down of the floor must continue.

We should be picking our crop in mid-April, when strawberries in the shops are almost worth their weight in gold.

For outdoor forcing, Dutch lights and cloches are used. It is a measure of the need for humus when forcing strawberries under Dutch lights and cloches that twenty-five years ago, one of the country's most renowned horticultural schools used partially decayed farmyard manure at the rate of 60 tons per acre as a pre-planting dressing, on a good medium loam which had probably been cultivated for 300 years or more. No gardener would have such cornucopian supplies, but the principle is worth remembering.

Having prepared the bed, we should add meat-and-bone meal at 4oz per sq yd. It is imperative to plan things so that the right number of plants at 18in apart can be fitted into each Dutch light frame when the frames are placed over the plants. Plants at the edges should not be crammed against the frames. A growing space of some 9in between the outer plants and the frame sides should be allowed. We can of course put the frames down first and plant into them, but it is better to plant pot grown runners into the open bed in late July, and place the frames over them at the end of the following February. Careful watering and adequate ventilation are needed. Ventilation is achieved by propping open each alternate light to a height of between about 3–6in depending on weather conditions. The warmer it is, the greater should be the gap; it is a great mistake to allow warmth at the expense of ventilation, since this leads to sappy growth and poor flower development. Six to seven hours per day of ventilation are required, with the lights being closed down before sun heat is lost in the late afternoon.

Full ventilation at flowering time is essential, and at this period lights should be propped open to the height of a brick's length, or more. At night straw can be laid over the lights against frost, or any sort of matting, even newspaper, will do. At petal fall the plants are given a thorough watering and then strawed down.

Ventilation is now reduced. On sunny days the plants are syringed three times daily throughout the swelling stage. Reduced ventilation does not mean suffocation. We must ensure enough air to obviate stagnation, and when the berries begin to colour, lights must be raised to 6in day and night, or removed by day if the weather is warm. If there is hot sunlight, lights should be left and sprayed thinly with limewash or flour and water to prevent sun scald.

Picking will normally commence about the third week of May in the south.

The other form of outdoor forcing, namely cloche culture, accommodates plants grown in rows. Under barn cloches or the flat topped kind, one row of plants 18in apart will fit nicely. Pre-planting work and time of planting are exactly as for Dutch lights.

Here again I would emphasise the value of early planting. The earlier we plant, the heavier will be the following year's crop, and the longer will the plants continue to fruit.

Planting after the first week in September is too late for a following year's crop in most circumstances; if such late work is unavoidable, the plants may still produce blossom the next spring, but it would be wise to remove the flowers.

With some varieties, especially Cambridge Vigour, a planting time that is relatively late but still early enough to give a maiden crop, often results in a light yield from that crop, but one that has the highest proportion of big berries.

So the best plan is to use the earliest August runners, which can either be pegged direct to the ground or into composition type pots filled with Levington compost, for planting into open ground, and the second lot of runners in late August or the first week in September for next year's cloching. In the south the earliest date for cloching is about the last week in February, with mid-March perhaps being ideal. It does not really matter when it is done between these dates, but cloches should not be in position before late February, since plants cloched earlier could suffer if there was a shortage of rain, unless they were removed and water was given, and nobody wants the bother of removing cloches if it can be avoided. The only logical exception to cloching between late February and mid-March may be where Red Core is a menace. Since this disease flourishes in wet conditions, winter cloching may help prevent its worst effects by maintaining relatively dry soil round the plants. However, this point, raised by workers at the Efford Experimental Station, relates more to professional growing than to gardening. We shall see in the section on diseases that reasonably effective measures against Red Core can be taken in gardens. The line should be unbroken, with each cloche touching its neighbour, and each end should be closed with a sheet of glass.

At flowering, every third cloche is removed to allow for pollination. In seasons of poor insect activity it would be wise to remove every alternate one. All removed cloches are replaced each evening (*see page* ??).

At petal fall cloches are removed, the plants are thoroughly watered and strawed down, and cloches replaced. As soon as the first fruits start to colour, the cloches should be arranged so that there is a 3in space between each, which means removing some to provide for this degree of ventilation. The space must be increased in hot weather, and thin lime wash in hot sunlight will, again, prevent scald.

To some extent, glass cloches are now giving way to continuous tunnels of plastic or polythene. These have gained favour on the continent, but results in Great Britain have not been spectacular. The covering is supported over wire hoops, or stapled to wooden battens. The latter method is finicky and time consuming, and so far has not proved worth the trouble.

I have tried both methods and do not like them, though I I must add that much longer rows were involved than would be in gardens. Crops were lighter, and berries more misshapen when compared with orthodox systems. Watering of long rows is difficult. A hose is essential, and it is a job to push it along the tunnels and achieve an even rate of water, though this applies much less to short rows. It has been claimed that moisture retention is sufficient to enable one to dispense with watering, but I doubt whether this is universally so. But the main problem seems to be pollination. Hive bees dislike confined spaces, in which they will not work very well, and it is possible that other insects are similarly put off. Claustrophobia may not be confined to humans. Also it is virtually impossible to exert any ventilation control over the tunnelled plants other than by rolling up the tunnels. They can in fact be rolled up and tied to a central bar running the length of the tunnel, where frames made on these lines are used (*see page 54*). This certainly obviates the pollination problem, but may be difficult to manage for ventilation if it has to be done frequently, and if the person who has to do it is out at work all day. Polythene with ventilation holes might overcome this problem.

Experiments are now in progress with tunnels of larger dimensions, presumably with a view to increasing ventilation. In the past, apparently good results were obtained from plants under continuous tunnels and using various methods of controlled ventilation, but it now seems certain that uncontrolled ventilation, ie complete freedom of air movement, is best during the blossom period. If polythene tunnels are used, it would be wise to have the type containing the central rib, so that the sides of the tunnel can be rolled up and tied to this at blossom time.

It is perhaps worth mentioning that apart from one or two

minor problems that are still not fully resolved, the culture of early crops under glass and in tunnels, and probably general culture in the open, has arrived, after years of experiment and many major developments in technique, at the stage where there is little more to be done. The developments have been absorbed into professional strawberry growing, and practically all of them can be taken advantage of by amateurs.

VI

Nutrition and Fertilisers

So far we have mentioned only meat-and-bone meal among the fertilisers. Levington and John Innes composts contain the necessary fertilisers in correctly balanced amounts, and no addition to these is normally needed. Meat-and-bone meal is mainly a comparatively slow acting nitrogen and phosphorus fertiliser containing an average of 11% phosphoric acid (P_2O_5), 7% nitrogen (N) and 1% potash (K_2O). Its phosphoric acid content is an aid to good root establishment, while nitrogen promotes growth, and potassium induces leaf efficiency and fruiting.

The whole subject of 'bag fertilisers' is fraught with contention among gardeners and we must spend a little time trying to sort out fact from fancy.

In general all fertilisers which are subjected to chemical processes of manufacture as distinct from being closely related in the popular mind to natural sources such as bones, fur, feathers, wool and treated sewage, are frequently regarded by organic enthusiasts as 'artificials', or are termed inorganic. From these enthusiasts they receive much condemnation, some of it justified, some not.

The 'artificial' quality of inorganics is said to ruin the flavour of fruit and edible crops in general, and to starve the soil or damage its structure.

In fact all fertilisers have an organic or 'natural' origin, whether derived from rock, soil deposits or air, and their constituents are the same as those derived from organic sources. But they are more concentrated, and being in granular or powder form, they contribute nothing to soil structure and may, as the organic school affirms, actually damage it, but only if used to excess or if applied to soil whose structure is poor to start with. In the latter case they may aggravate existing unsatisfactory conditions by increasing still further the sticky nature of the soil.

Where inorganics are applied year after year in the absence of compost, certain soil types, especially light ones, will quite definitely become impoverished, and in order to boost the crops it will become necessary to use ever increasing amounts of fertiliser. The soil then becomes akin to that used in sand culture and other forms of experimental work where plant nutrition is solely a matter of applied chemistry, and where the rooting medium is little more than something for the roots to hold on to. In some experimental work even this is dispensed with, and the plants are fitted into bottles and so forth and grown entirely in nutrient solutions. In fact, this type of culture, known as hydroponics, is now well established in many parts of the world.

Now let us have firmly in mind the following points. Wholesale condemnation of inorganics lies in the realm of fancy; their judicious use, when they are regarded as a supplementary means of providing our strawberry plants with essential nutrients that cannot always be taken up from the soil in the right amounts and at the periods when they are needed, lies in the realm of common sense. We have to bear in mind that nutrients possessed by compost and organic fertilisers and manures are nearly always slow acting, which means that their availability is spread over long periods, and that they may not be absorbed in sufficient quantities at those times when the plants' demands on them are at their greatest. Also they are present in amounts that are small when compared with those possessed by inorganics.

We return to the earlier hypothesis that organic matter is not primarily food for the plants, but a means of establishing those soil conditions under which food is most freely available. Organic matter lays the foundation of soil fertility, and to some extent provides nourishment, but it is not always enough in itself.

A brief consideration of the nutrient contents of some

organic and inorganic manures and fertilisers will make things clearer, so I give a table showing the average analysis of various manurial products. Those termed organic are of course different from 'organic matter' in the form of compost, and possess fairly well defined values for their respective nutrients.

Organic	N	Percentage P_2O_5	Compositions K_2O
Basic Slag	–	6–18	–
Steamed Bone Flour	1–2	25–32	–
Bone Meal	3.5–5.0	20–25	–
Fish Meal	7–9	7–9	–
Wood Ash	–	–	6
Meat and Bone Meal	6–8	11	1
Dried Blood	12	1	0.5
Hoof and Horn Meal	12–14	2.5	–
Soot	3	–	–
Shoddy	3–14	–	–
Seaweed Fresh	0.5	0.1	1
Dried	1.4	0.4	2.6
Farmyard Manure Cow	0.34	0.16	0.4
Horse	0.58	0.28	0.53
Pig	0.45	0.19	0.60
Poultry	1.6	1.79	0.66
Inorganic (fresh)			
Sulphate of Potash	–	–	50
Muriate of Potash	–	–	60
Superphosphate (granular)	–	19	–
(powder)	–	18	–
Triple Superphosphate	–	47	–
Sulphate of Ammonia	21	–	–
Nitro Chalk	15.5–21	–	–
Nitrate of Soda	16	–	–

Since potassium is the most important element for strawberries as far as applications are concerned, we can usefully compare wood ash with sulphate of potash, when we find that the latter contains approximately eight times the value of the former. The lesson here is that if our strawberry plants are deficient in potassium we can rarely hope to make good the lack by shovelling on ash from the bonfire, but we can certainly tackle the trouble by giving sulphate of potash. Many times I have come up against this very problem among gardeners who have been assured that wood ash is the answer. It is not, and to say that it is will get the unfortunate plants nowhere. Sometimes its potassium content may be as low as 1%.

Nitrogen is now known to be needed by strawberries in far smaller quantities than was once thought, and it has been found that in excess it encourages foliage at the expense of fruit, besides sometimes lowering the quality of the berries, and rendering the plants more prone to certain diseases. In fact in many instances applied nitrogen is unnecessary; where this is so, its use will do no good but may do harm. The addition of meat-and-bone meal as previously advocated is safe, because this fertiliser also contains two other substances which the plants need and which should not only neutralise any adverse effects of nitrogen but should also ensure that nutritional balance in which the elements complement each other, a state where each is performing a specific function necessary to the well being of the plants.

Balance is the crux of the matter. Nutritional troubles consequent upon applied fertilisers almost invariably arise as a result of imbalance between the elements absorbed. Excessive nitrogen leads to a deficiency of potash and often of magnesium, and this principle of one element in excess cancelling or partly cancelling another one out applies generally in the field of plant nutrition.

Apart from dried seaweed, which is used at about half the rate of ordinary compost, ie $\frac{1}{2}$cwt to 12sq yd as a pre-planting dressing, none of the organics in the table will satisfy the demand for a balanced feed throughout the cropping life of strawberries. Meat-and-bone meal is a useful aid to early establishment, but for later periods it is too high in nitrogen and phosphorus relative to potash. The same lack of balance is found among the others. (I am excluding the animal manures, which would normally be used in composting, and would not therefore be regarded as having a direct nutritional effect.)

None of the organics would be very satisfactory for correcting mineral deficiencies, partly because they would not act quickly enough, and partly because they might upset the general nutrient balance.

The policy I have always adopted is to withhold fertilisers, except in the case of meat-and-bone for forced plants, until deficiency symptoms first appear (often they do not appear at all) when the appropriate fertiliser is given as soon as the need arises. But for those who want a general fertiliser recommendation in the absence of pre-planting dung or compost, this is 1oz sulphate of ammonia, 2oz superphosphate, 1oz sulphate of potash, all per sq yd.

It is, I think, a sound policy to withhold fertilisers where the soil is fertile and promotes good plant growth in general, but it will fail if deficiency symptoms are ignored or go unrecognised. So our next job is to consider visual symptoms of deficiencies and the means of making these good. Here it must be appreciated that the three nutrients given in the tables do not exhaust the plants' needs. There are several micro-nutrients, zinc, boron, copper etc, known as trace elements, which are vital to health, but most of these are present in soils in the minute quantities required, and for all practical purposes we are concerned only with the major ones.

NUTRITIONAL DEFICIENCIES

We have already seen that the leaves are the plant's factory. Manufacturing cannot proceed in the absence of the necessary materials. Where these are absent, the factory will tell us so; in other words the leaves will show deficiency symptoms.

Unfortunately, some doubt as to the degree of deficiency is inevitable. Only leaf analysis will show the actual content of nutritional elements, and will determine the difference between existing and optimum levels, and this is obviously beyond the amateur's resources. However, enough experience has been amassed over the years to provide gardeners with a reasonably accurate guide as to the amounts of fertiliser to apply.

We should realise that modern, virus-tested plants, ie those certified free of known virus diseases at the time of sale, have lower requirements for nitrogen and phosphorus than plants had years ago, before there was a virus testing and certification scheme.

NITROGEN

This is the basis of plant growth. Fundamentally, we can say that it promotes leaf size and makes for strong flower buds. It is very mobile in the leaves and readily passes from older foliage to new, that is to the young, actively growing points. In other words the leaf content in the older foliage will supplement that already existing in the young, and we are not likely to see severe deficiency symptoms in the plant so long as the young leaves are sufficient in nitrogen.

Nevertheless, if the nitrogen content of the young leaves has to be appreciably supplemented by that of the older ones, it can point to a lack somewhere in the plant. Recent work on this subject showed that lack of nitrogen did not inhibit flower initiation, but did inhibit the formation of branch crowns. Since crops depend on crown growth and on the number of flowers produced by each crown, it is easily seen that if crown growth is inhibited, yields will be small.

The signs of nitrogen deficiency are yellowing of the leaves, often with tints of red or purple. Where it is severe, leaf growth will be poor, and blossoms weak and unable to set the berries. Thus although flower production may not be reduced, the ability of the flowers to set fruit may be diminished.

PHOSPHORUS

Although there appears to be a close correlation between nitrogen and phosphorus in strawberries, it is rare for a deficiency of the latter to be severe enough to become evident in normally grown plants. Deficiencies can be induced in experimental work, when the effects are similar to those caused by low nitrogen, but for practical gardening purposes we can take it that phosphorus will not be lacking.

POTASSIUM

This is without doubt the element that is most likely to be in short supply, especially on light soils. It is closely related to water movement in the plant, a shortage is most severe where drainage is too free. It can also be deficient where drainage is impeded; in this case the absorbing roots are killed, and we have a perfect example of poverty amidst plenty. The plant needs water but cannot get it because an excess has drowned the feeding hairs and cut off the supply route.

The clearest indication of potash deficiency is a greyish, brittle margin to the leaves. Often leaf colour becomes bluish-green, and leaf growth is checked. Flowers are weak and berries are small and flavourless.

IRON

This is normally regarded as a trace element, but deficiencies can be very marked on alkaline soils, and in these circumstances iron becomes very much a major element, since without it the plants will fail miserably. Iron deficiency markedly reduces flower production, and to a lesser extent reduces berry size.

There is sometimes a difference between the cause of iron shortage in plants and the cause of shortage of the major elements. The latter are likely to be missing from the soil; iron is not necessarily absent in the soil—indeed as a trace element it is probably present—but on alkaline soil there is a reaction known as lime induced chlorosis, which is expressed as lack of iron. In strongly alkaline soils the calcium inhibits the uptake of iron, when the tip leaves show a distinct pattern of chlorosis, or yellowing. The leaf blade is yellow, but with the vein network standing out in clear relief.

Page 89 (above) Tortrix Caterpillar damage;
(below) Tortrix Caterpillar ×24 (approx)

(above) Blossom Weevil damage showing two partly severed flower stalks hanging

Page 90

(left) Flower stalk puncture by Blossom Weevil

In plants suffering from induced iron deficiency this element moves slowly, so that the most obvious symptoms occur in leaves at shoot tips, and are progressively less marked on lower leaves. Strawberry leaves do not of course occur in series along a shoot, but in rosettes at the ends of leaf stalks, and we shall find symptoms of chlorosis mainly on young leaves. Where the trouble is severe the vein pattern may become obscured, when the leaves assume an ivory white colour, often with dead, brown patches (necrosis) along the margins.

MANGANESE

This element is not often lacking but it must be mentioned because confusion between iron and manganese deficiency is very easy. Again, chlorosis is the prominent feature, but manganese is more mobile than iron, and tip leaves often remain normal, with deficiency symptoms more or less confined to lower ones. The yellowing begins near the leaf margin and creeps towards the midrib in a fairly well defined V-shaped pattern, with the main and lateral veins remaining green, but without the net-work effect of iron deficiency. If the shortage becomes severe, the vein pattern may vanish.

MAGNESIUM

This is intimately connected with chlorophyll, the green colouring matter of leaves. Where it is absent the foliage will show various colours other than green. In magnesium deficient plants the element does not move from old leaves to young, but remains in the former as a fixed amount that is below the optimum. As the leaves increase in size the deficiency becomes evident.

We have here an example of how a deficiency of one element can be induced by an excess of another. If nitrogen is applied to the extent where it encourages undue leaf growth, the magnesium content, which may be enough to satisfy leaves of normal size, may be insufficient for the increased growth. The areas lacking magnesium will then take on various unnatural colours and will eventually turn brown and die.

F

This is another element that is more generally lacking, whether the lack is induced or not, on light, freely drained soils that are low in humus.

Magnesium shortage is, unfortunately, one of the most difficult to determine from visual symptoms, except perhaps in certain tree fruits, because it can show many different effects. Interveinal necrosis, when brown, longitudinal areas lie distinctly between the veins, is almost a classic sign, but there may be brown leaf margins, different from the ashy colour denoting lack of potassium, and varying shades of yellow or red on the foliage. We can, however, draw some comfort from the fact that magnesium is not often lacking in strawberries, and also that modest measures aimed at correcting a deficiency will do little or no harm where there is already enough and where the trouble was wrongly diagnosed.

Such are the nutritional elements with which gardeners are most commonly concerned. We will now examine ways of making good any deficiencies.

The first thing to understand is that where foliage sprays of the various elements are feasible, this method is preferable to their application in fertiliser form. Speed is essential, and the materials will be absorbed into the leaf factory much more quickly through the leaves than through the roots. We bypass the translocation process via soil and roots and we do not have to wait for the solvent effects of soil moisture.

Nitrogen is made good by spraying with urea at a rate of 2oz in $2\frac{1}{2}$gal water at fortnightly intervals from the time when deficiency symptoms first appeared. As I have implied, excess is to be strongly avoided, and as soon as it is evident that the plants are responding and that leaf yellowing has disappeared, spraying must stop. If foliar applications cannot be made, apply nitro chalk at rate of $\frac{3}{4}$–1oz per sq yd on acid soils, or sulphate of ammonia at the same rate on alkaline ones.

Potash deficiency is corrected by soil applications of sulphate of potash at rate of $\frac{1}{2}$–1oz per sq yd.

Iron treatment is probably best carried out by using iron

chelate strictly to maker's advice. It can either be applied to the soil or sprayed on to the foliage. In the latter case the usual treatment is ¼oz chelate in 25pt water at fortnightly intervals until symptoms disappear, but this is only a guide, and is not to be taken in preference to the advice on the bottle, if this should be different.

Manganese, as we have seen, is unlikely to be lacking, but if deficiency treatment does become necessary, spray with 1½oz manganese sulphate in 2½gal water. Two, or at most three, applications, with 14 days between them, should suffice.

Magnesium is applied to foliage as commercial grade Epsom Salt (magnesium sulphate) at rate of 8oz in 2½gal water, two or three sprays at 14-day intervals being the average. This is somewhat porridge-like solution, and if it is beyond the scope of the sprayer the only thing to do is to halve the rate and give twice the number of applications at 7-day intervals.

In order to get urea, manganese sulphate and Epsom Salt to stick to the foliage it is advisable to include a wetting agent. There are several brands of these on the market, or a little soft soap or a squirt of Fairy liquid can be used instead, but do not use any form of detergent. Fertilisers must be applied carefully, to the soil only, and not to the plants, and if the weather is dry they should be well watered in.

I have to admit that it is easier for me to write about these problems than it is for some people to resolve them in the garden. This statement is not intended as a slur on anyone's intelligence. No matter how detailed the descriptions of nutrient deficiency symptoms, some confusion is inevitable until one has gained experience. In fact it often exists among professional growers. For this reason I would mention that the all-purpose foliar feeds based on seaweed are a useful proposition for gardeners who are not quite sure of themselves.

Seaweed—which is a good manure—contains in foliar feed solution most of the trace elements needed. I have an innate suspicion of 'all purpose' compounds in horticulture, because plant needs vary enormously, and it is difficult to see how any one substance can satisfy every type of plant. I would not say

that a particular nutrient deficiency could be invariably corrected by seaweed spraying, but I will say that these sprays
provide a worthwhile tonic, or may prevent deficiency symptoms from appearing.

Seaweed varies in its constituents and perhaps seaweed
sprays vary in the same way, but a good quality brand has a
satisfactory analysis and in spite of its relatively high price, is
economical to use because only small amounts of neat material
are required. One of the leading makers recommends a spray
on commercially grown strawberries at 3gal of neat liquid per
acre as fruit trusses appear, repeated when the first fruits set.
Six gallons per acre is about $\frac{1}{8}$pt to $12\frac{1}{2}$sq yd. At 18×30in
this area would take 30 plants. So we can hardly complain
that spraying at the rate of about 1/128pt per plant is extrava-
gant.

The dilution rate is immaterial. All we need do is to pour
out the neat liquid into the sprayer at the rate of $\frac{1}{8}$pt to $12\frac{1}{2}$
sq yd (or at whatever rate the particular maker recommends)
and then top up with water to the required total amount of
liquid. Since seaweed sprays are quite harmless, there is no
need to work to exact limits; if the neat rate is above that
given, or if more dilute liquid goes on than was intended,
there will be no adverse effects.

LIME

Lime is the material many of us are apt to scatter over the
garden without exactly knowing why. It is a 'soil sweetener',
it assists flocculation, has a mysteriously liberating power and
so on. All these things are true, and they invest it with a
comforting security, a feeling that you can't go wrong by adding lime. But with strawberries you can go wrong, for unless
the soil is markedly acid they do not need it, and a basic tenet
of plant husbandry should be not to give plants things they
do not need.

Lime supplies calcium, and is therefore a plant food as well
as a soil conditioner. The calcium content of soil is measured

by the pH value, the figure 7.0 indicating neutrality. Values below that show acidity, and those above, alkalinity.

To be strictly accurate, the values refer to the soil water. This contains varying proportions of ions of hydrogen and hydroxyl; neutral solutions contain equal numbers of these ions, acid ones have more hydrogen than hydroxyl, and the reverse applies to alkaline solutions.

The pH figure does not illustrate a common denominator applicable to every soil type, but only the degree of acidity or alkalinity of any particular type, so corrective treatments vary according to the nature of the soil. They also vary in accordance with the form of lime being used. If, for example, we are correcting acidity with ground quicklime, the amounts in ounces to apply per square yard on various soils to bring the pH up to 5.5 to 6.0 would be approximately as follows:

Existing pH	Sand	Light Loam	Medium Loam	Heavy Loam
4.0	5	7	9	11
4.5	3	5	7	9
5.0	2	3	5	7

If we were using hydrated lime we should apply $1\frac{1}{3}$oz for each ounce of quicklime, or 2oz if we were using finely ground chalk.

Soil testing kits are now available, which are a great improvement on the old trick of pouring hydrochloric acid on to the soil to see if it bubbled. This showed whether lime was required, but gave no guidance as to how much.

Strawberries will tolerate a pH range of about 1.0 to 2.0, or say between pH 4.0 and 6.0, with the ideal being about 5.5. This last figure is approximately the lowest optimum for the full activity of nitrifying organisms, which means that below it these may not work to full capacity, with the result that available nitrogen may be deficient, perhaps not severely enough to be expressed in leaf symptoms, but enough to have some adverse effect on growth.

Phosphates are freely available when the pH is at 5.5. If it is below this, or above 7.5, phosphates become locked up in varying degrees, and will not get to the plants in adequate amounts. Again, visual symptoms will not necessarily show, and more probably will not. In this event the plants may suffer without our being able to diagnose the reason. Where acidity is severe, available calcium and magnesium will be insufficient, but this is unlikely on garden soils within the range of those suitable for strawberries.

The best advice I can give is to regard lime not as being automatically necessary for strawberries, but ideally to use a soil tester first, and to work to a pH of 5.5. In the absence of a tester, omit lime if the cabbages are doing well, for these are good indicators.

Another way of looking at it is to consider the ounces of quicklime needed per square yard to raise the pH by 1.0, this being, on average, the range within which we would work. The amounts on sandy, loamy, and clayey soils according to their organic content would be approximately:

Soil	Low in Organics	High in Organics
Sandy	2	9
Loamy	8	16
Clayey	12	18

We see from these figures that, above a certain point, organic content increases acidity to the stage where, at least on loamy and clayey soils, relatively high dressings of quicklime, and proportionately heavier ones of the milder forms, would be needed to achieve a more satisfactory pH value. On soils low in organic content less lime is needed to raise the pH by 1.0, but of course this does not necessarily mean that such an increase would be adequate, though it might be.

The golden mean is, as always, the best; manurial or compost dressings at rates mentioned earlier will normally suffice for the life of an individual strawberry plot, and will very seldom prove to be high enough to cause excess acidity.

If lime has to be used, the best time is before planting. Liming is in fact a pre-planting measure, and not one to be carried out after the plants are in.

PART III

VII

Pests and Diseases: The Background

We now turn to another aspect of spraying, namely pest and disease control, so let us brace ourselves for further battles, for perhaps no branch of gardening is more misunderstood, or is subject to more well intentioned but misguided opinion.

There are two fundamental principles to observe; pests are *controlled*; diseases are *prevented*. The two may seem the same, but they are not, so let us see how they differ.

Pests in general make their presence known before they have done significant damage. They are clearly visible; we can see that they are there, and in many cases we can see the damage they are doing, and even watch them doing it. There are exceptions, especially in relation to strawberry aphids (greenfly) for these transmit virus disease, and we cannot observe a virus, save under an electron microscope, which few of us possess, since they are apt to cost around thirty to forty thousand pounds. Nevertheless, the principle applies throughout the common range of pests.

This means that there is no point in spraying against pests until they appear. Anticipation can lead to much needless spraying. When they do appear, we spray, provided they are present in numbers justifying an insecticide, or if we cannot adequately control them with finger and thumb. We cannot, logically, control activities that have not begun, but we can control them from the point at which they begin.

The concept of control does of course apply also to diseases inasmuch as we can strive to stop them spreading, but fundamentally we seek to prevent their occurrence. The reason for prevention of disease, as distinct from control of pests, is that prevention, in the form of a fungicidal layer of protection over the plant, either stops fungus spores from germinating on the plant surface, or stops the mycelium arising from germination from penetrating the plant tissues. Once this penetration has occurred, infection can be destroyed only by systemic fungicides, which work in the sap stream of the plant. These are being developed, and at least one has given good trial results against certain diseases.

Briefly, the cycle of fungus infection is as follows. Spores alight on the plant surface, germinate, and produce tiny threads of growing points, or mycelium. These penetrate within the cells, feeding on their contents. Later the fruiting or fructification stage is reached, when 'fruiting bodies' appear on the plant. These are sacs, containing more spores. They burst open to liberate their contents, and the cycle is renewed.

There are many variations according to the species of fungus, its relationship to weather (eg strawberry mildew is largely a dry weather disease, while botrytis is a wet weather one) and the fruiting bodies assume a wide variety of shapes, sizes and forms, again according to species. But we may take the process as outlined here as being common to the leaf and fruit fungi.

There are also root fungi, whose mode of perpetuation is basically the same, but which in some cases have an extremely prolonged life in the soil. The devastating Red Core, for example, can lie dormant for at least thirteen years, even in the absence of strawberries, waiting to infect new plants.

If a leaf fungus has penetrated the plant, we cannot eradicate it from its immediate area, but we can apply fungicides to protect other areas and fresh leaves from becoming infected at the spore liberation stage that follows mycelium growth. But this is more difficult than it may sound. We cannot judge the moment at which fruiting bodies will appear, so we have no sure guide as to the time to spray. However, modern fungicides are sufficiently persistent to allow us to spray as soon as infection is seen, in the knowledge that a protective layer will be present when the spores are disseminated, though it is frequently necessary to spray at intervals in order to ensure that the entire phase of spore liberation is covered.

It is in their failure to appreciate the necessity for several sprays that amateurs so often go astray. Time after time one hears of a single application having been made, as though this were some magic potion expected to protect the plants throughout the entire season. This misapprehension stems from a lack of understanding of the ways of plant diseases. A single does of medicine will seldom cure a disease of the human body; the same principle applies to plants. They need a course of treatment, though in their case it is prevention rather than cure that we should aim at.

This should not frighten us into imagining that we have got to be constantly spraying. On the contrary, provided the protection is given in time, before the disease has entered the plant, only a few applications will be needed, and of course there are seasons when no sprays will be called for, particularly where the more resistant varieties are grown.

The concept of systemic insecticides against sap sucking pests is well established. Here we can spray with materials which attack the pests from within the plant. These sprays contain substances toxic to the pests, but not to humans. Aphids and other sap suckers absorb the toxic ingredients with the sap. In some ways these materials are the safest of any, because once inside the plant they affect only pests; they do not kill the main beneficial species, since these do not feed on the plant, but on the plant pests. In my own mind, and doubtless in the minds of others, there is a nagging fear that predators feeding on poisoned prey may themselves imbibe some poison from the latter, in the same way that predatory birds take up toxic doses from prey killed by certain sprays. However, there seems at present little evidence that this does happen, though my own feeling is that much more work on this aspect is necessary before these doubts can be resolved with certainty.

Personally, I do not use systemic insecticides if I can do without them. I confine myself to such materials as derris, pyrethrum and the semi-systemic malathion. The first two are entirely contact insecticides; the latter is partly a contact and partly a systemic one. The toxicity of all three to humans, birds and domestic pets (except fish) is virtually non-existent; derris and pyrethrum may be used up to harvest—though their use at anything like so late a period is never, or almost never, called for, while malathion may be used up to twenty four hours before harvest. Derris and pyrethrum, and probably malathion, spell certain death to fish, and no drift must be allowed into streams or ponds. But fish are the only 'domesticated' creatures so affected.

EFFECTS ON BENEFICIAL SPECIES

Apart from such obvious creatures as bees, which are essential for the pollination of strawberry flowers, there is a wide range of insects, some of which are also pollinators, and many of which are very valuable as pest controlling agents, since they are either predacious or parasitic upon plant enemies. In effect, both types are predacious, inasmuch as prey constitutes their food, but the division is used to distinguish between those that attack from the outside and those that attack from within.

Among the former are such things as ladybirds and their larvae, the larvae of hoverflies (those wasp-like but non-stinging flies that hover on rapidly beating wings, and suddenly dart off to hover again) and larvae of the beautiful and delicate lacewing flies (*see page 71*). Various species of 'bugs' anthocorids, capsids etc, especially the 'black-kneed' capsid, are extremely valuable. These consume their prey from the outside, and in some cases the eggs also, by sucking out their contents. The parasites, often comprising minute flies, lay eggs in the soft bodies of their prey, generally when the prey are in the larval stage. The eggs hatch, and the parasites live as larvae within the prey, feeding on the tissues and body juices.

This is a vast subject involving hundreds of species, which would need a separate volume to do it justice. The fact that we can do no more here than give it passing mention does not mean that it is unimportant. An appreciation of the fact that biological control is part of nature's pattern is absolutely essential to a rational approach to human control.

Predators and parasites are quite indispensable; they do not always effect total control, for a number of reasons. Prey may be inadequate to sustain predators early in the season, in which event the latter will either die or go elsewhere; pest populations may swamp those of the predators, when only very limited control will be achieved; weather conditions may not affect pests adversely, but may be unfavourable to predators. In spite of these possible snags, however, every effort should be made to encourage beneficial insects, which mean reducing sprays to the absolute minimum consistent with adequate control, and confining their use to those materials that are known to cause the least harm.

Probably any spray that kills a pest will also kill a predator, but danger to the latter is greatly reduced if non-residual materials like those already noted are used. If these hit a predator they will probably kill it, which is exceedingly unfortunate for those in the larval stage, since they cannot escape the spray. However, many beneficial species are actively on the wing and these often do escape. Provided no insecticides are ever sprayed on to open blossom, actively pollinating insects will not suffer. Sometimes fungicides overlap the flowering period in certain circumstances, but are rarely applied at full flower, and in any case those I shall advocate do not appear to be unduly harmful.

DDT, now banned from gardens, was the classic example of a residual insecticide having virtually no selectivity and therefore being toxic to friend and foe alike. Its withdrawal should go a long way towards preserving predators and parasites.

The sprays I recommend, with the partial exception of malathion, have a very short residual period. They are meant to achieve nearly instant control of the pests they are aimed at, and not to leave deposits which may later be picked up by predators. The only significant residual effect of malathion lies in its semi-systemic properties, and as we have seen, these do not affect our insect friends (at least as far as we know).

In the use of the contact materials derris and pyrethrum, we must appreciate that two sprays, the second some 5–7 days after the first, are sometimes needed against aphids. In some seasons three sprays might have to be used. The reason is that throughout the entire summer aphids are born as living young, and although the sprays will kill the adult females, they will not necessarily kill unborn young the females may be carrying. Because there is only a short lived residue, the young will often not emerge on to a poisoned surface, but will survive. Even when they emerge on to a surface covered with dry deposits of derris or pyrethrum, they will probably not succumb, since to be effective these materials must, in liquid form, cover the pests. They will of course survive the mother's death only if they are in a sufficiently advanced stage and are at the point of birth, but this happens frequently, and explains why amateurs so often fail to control greenfly with one spray application. They then blame the spray, and turn to some other more persistent substances, like BHC, thus starting on the downward path to perdition, the one that leads to the slaughter of the innocents, for BHC is almost as deadly to predators as DDT.

To sum up the philosophy of pest and disease control, we can reduce matters to the simple theme of minimum spraying consistent with adequate control, using materials known to be the least harmful to beneficial species, and *never* increasing the mixing rate above that recommended by the maker. This is an important point. For some obscure reason amateurs often add a bit more 'just to make sure.' We may be quite certain that the manufacturers would not recommend less than they have to; to go above the stated rate is merely to throw money away, and possibly to cause harm. Sometimes minimum and maximum rates are quoted, eg 2–4oz; usually the smaller is enough, with the larger being reserved for serious outbreaks, or where some pest or disease has become established. Where these conditions do not apply, the smaller amount will usually suffice, but if in doubt, take the average of the two figures.

We will now examine the major pests and diseases, and this is an appropriate moment for me to repeat something I have said more than once over the years, where fruit pests are concerned—If you don't know it, leave it; it's probably a friend.

VIII

Major Pests

APHIDS (GREENFLY)

Although at least four species of aphids breed on strawberries, and many more appear from time to time, only two are of major importance, namely the Strawberry Aphid, *Pentatrichopus fragaefolii*, and the Shallot Aphid, *Myzus ascalonicus*.

The first is creamy white with knobbed hairs on its back, easily seen under a 10x lens. (A good lens is essential for the identification of most pests). The aphids are less than $\frac{1}{12}$in long and are found chiefly on the undersides of young unfolding leaves. Wingless specimens are present throughout the year, breeding continuously except in severe weather. On established plants wingless aphids are present in greatest numbers in early summer. They then decline swiftly to remain fairly low until the following summer. On maiden plants peak populations are reached later, usually in September. Winged forms are found mainly in May and June, with smaller numbers in autumn and winter. There is a flight to other plants in these two months, this being the primary dispersal period, though some dispersal may also occur in autumn.

This species is a transmitter of the virus diseases known as Crinkle and Yellow Edge, to which Royal Sovereign is very susceptible. The supreme importance which these virus diseases held for many years is somewhat lessened today with the breeding of more tolerant or more resistant varieties of strawberries, but it is still just as essential as formerly to control the transmitting aphids. Varieties do not necessarily remain resistant to the original viruses, added to which is the fact that the viruses can evolve new strains having the power to infect plants that repelled the original strain.

106

(*above*) Vine
Weevil Grubs,
× 12 (approx).
Note typically
curved posture

Page 107

(*right*) Netted
strawberry bed

Page 108 *(above)* Botrytis (Greymould) on strawberries;
(below) strawberry leaf spot

It is essential to recognise that virus transmitting aphids demand a much greater degree of control than do species causing only mechanical damage. As long as the former remain on the plants the danger of infection is present.

The other primary aphid, the Shallot species, is pale brownish or greenish brown, with slender 'honey tubes' that are slightly swollen towards the tips. These appendages, which all aphids possess and which vary a little in length, size and sometimes colour, according to species, bear their popular name for the reason that excess sugar absorbed by the aphids from the cell sap is excreted through the tubes on to the leaf. There it causes the familiar sticky deposit, on which a sooty looking fungus usually forms. The leaves are therefore subjected to two distinct forms of damage. The sticky deposit blocks the pores, and the fungal deposit completes the process, so that the efficient functioning of the leaves is made impossible. Where, in addition to these factors, virus is also transmitted, the plant stands no chance at all.

The Shallot Aphid is also a virus vector, though whether of strawberry viruses is by no means an established certainty. What it does very definitely cause is a severe stunting of the plants; attacked leaves become badly distorted and turn brown. Where isolated plants or small blocks of plants are affected, they stand out in sharp contrast to healthy ones.

The damage first appears in May and remains visible until July. Although plants may recover later, they will produce nothing to speak of in the season of attack, and will be so weakened that their subsequent performance will be seriously impaired.

Infestation first occurs in autumn, when the first brood of young (nymphs) is deposited by winged forms. Breeding continues during winter and spring, giving rise to a succession of wingless generations until May or early June, when winged forms appear which fly off to various other host plants. The wingless aphids colonise the young crown leaves as these unfold in spring, and later the blossom trusses. Only a few are found on mature leaves at this time, which means that inspec-

G

tion of the main sites is necessary for the determination of colonies.

This species appears to be considerably more susceptible to hard winters than the first mentioned, though this too will succumb to severe weather. It is invariably present in greater numbers in spring after a mild winter. I must point out that, important as this aphid is when it occurs, it is a sporadic species. Particularly after severe winters, it may be absent, and even mild winters do not necessarily mean that aphids will appear the following spring. Even so, it is advisable to check for aphids every spring, in case the other species is present.

Other types that occur from time to time are the Glasshouse Potato, the Potato and Violet Aphids, none of which is of much importance. However, among these, occurs a species having no popular name but known botanically as *Acyrthosiphon malvae*, which is a vector of certain viruses, though not a very efficient one. It is unlikely that most amateurs would distinguish this from the Potato aphid, and as it can transmit virus to some extent, this is a good reason for controlling all aphids, whether or not we suspect them of being dangerous.

Here I must try to make clear the position regarding 'virus tested plants', for it is evidently misunderstood by many amateurs. These are plants raised under the strict conditions of the official Certification Scheme. We need not go into this, except to say that plants whose raising has fulfilled the obligations of this scheme are inspected by Ministry of Agriculture inspectors and if found free of known viruses are certified as such. This means that they are virus free at the time of sale. It does *not* mean that they will necessarily remain so after they have left the nursery. From that time the onus is entirely on the buyer. It is up to him to keep his plants free of virus by controlling the insect vectors. Either derris, pyrethrum or malathion will control aphids. The young plants can be dipped in the appropriate solution before planting, as an initial safeguard. Whether or not this is done, plants should be inspected periodically, most particularly in early spring, and sprayed if necessary.

BEETLES

The most important beetle pest is the Strawberry Seed Beetle, *Harpalus rufipes*. It is between $\frac{1}{2}$–$\frac{3}{4}$in long, with a greyish-golden 'finish' and red legs. It is very active and runs rapidly when disturbed. As its name implies, it removes the 'seeds', actually the achenes complete with seeds, thus causing malformation (*see page 71*). It also attacks the receptacle, biting out pieces and leaving holes that are frequently attributed by gardeners to birds and slugs.

There are also three shiny, black species, all with black legs, and a sub-species that is black with red legs, and there is one that varies from green to a coppery and purplish colour, all having grooved wing cases. One sub-species again has red legs. Finally there is a black one with red feelers and legs, sometimes with black knees, and always with visibly pitted lines on the wing cases.

These beetles lay egg batches below the soil surface during summer, at an average rate of fifteen eggs per batch. The grubs hunt actively for soil prey, but also feed on vegetation. Both grubs and adults hibernate in the soil, becoming active again in spring. All species are at home among leaf litter, weeds and general debris, and the basic control measure is cleanliness.

Unfortunately, there is no safe insecticide that will deal with these pests, with the possible exception of malathion. This did give encouraging results in tests, though it was not clear whether the substance was wholly toxic and partly repellent. What did emerge was that canned fruits that had been sprayed were tainted in some degree, so the experiments were abandoned. Some beetles can be trapped in jam jars of hay etc, removed each morning and inspected, since the beetles are mainly nocturnal, but the best way is to discourage them by keeping the plot and its surrounds free of debris. Another method is to surround the plot in spring with a fence of polythene film.

In one trial samples of fruit from 48 plants inside the fence and from the same number just outside, taken in late June and early July, gave an average of 3 damaged berries from inside the fence, and 50 from outside. The barrier consisted of 12in 'layflat' polythene tubing 0.002in thick, supported at the top edge by a strand of galvanised wire, and with the bottom edge buried 3in in the soil. Wooden posts supported the wire, set at an angle of 60° outwards, to give an outward sloping fence to prevent the beetles from climbing up.

A trench about 4in deep is opened up round the plot with the vertical wall on the inside, about 3ft from the plants. Posts are driven in, sloping outwards, at the corners. The end of the tubing is fastened to a corner post, and the tube reeled out along the trench. The supporting wire is then threaded through it. The base of the tubing is firmly buried in the trench, the wire lightly stapled to the corner post about 8in above the soil, drawn taut, to raise the fence, and then fixed by driving the staple firmly home. Two people are needed for the job. The entire plot is enclosed in the same way. The polythene being led round the corner posts.

The fence should be erected in late April, before the movement of beetles into the strawberry bed has begun.

CHAFER BEETLES

These are well known species that include the Rose Chafer and the large, zooming May-bug, which crashes about lighted rooms at night during May and June, and is named *Melolontha melolontha*. It is the grubs of all these chafers that cause damage in strawberry beds, by eating the roots, and thus killing the plants, or at least making them wilt severely.

The female May-bug lays from 60-70 eggs in the soil in May and June. The grubs spend up to four or possibly five years in the ground, and are fat, white and curled, with a brown head. Finally they enter the chrysalis stage, and the adults later emerge. It is often found that May-bugs occur heavily in one season, and then fail to appear for several years. The reason is that the intervening years are spent in the grub stage.

Whenever a strawberry plant is wilting, unless the reason is drought, the chafer grub should be suspected. If they are the cause they will be found among the root soil of the lifted plant, though it may be necessary to dig down 6–8in.

Again, chemical control is out for the gardener, with the possible exception of BHC dust, but this may taint the fruit, and so is not suitable for fruiting beds. The best method is to dig up the grubs when preparing the soil. Usually this will suffice for the life of the bed.

CAPSIDS

The Common Green Capsid, *Lygus pabulinus*, is perhaps not widespread on strawberries at present, but is sufficiently important where it does occur to warrant treatment. It probably became prominent in the Wisbech area of Cambridgeshire, but is certainly not confined to that region. The adult is about $\frac{1}{4}$in long, with pale green wings, lighter at the tips, held flat over the body when the insect is resting. Overwintered eggs hatch in late April or early May, and the nymphs start to feed by sucking juice from the leaves. Adults feed likewise, the attacked areas showing as small reddish and brown spots near the midrib. As the leaves expand these spots can be seen as small holes. Fruits are also attacked, leading to malformation. All stages of this bug are very active. Both nymphs and adults run rapidly for cover when disturbed, this being a certain feature that distinguishes them from green species of aphids, with which they are sometimes confused. Adults also take wing when disturbed, though they do not fly far. There are two generations a year; in general, the second infests other host plants, the adults flying to these first for egg laying, but sometimes this generation occurs on the original plant, ie the strawberry, and remains there for the rest of its season. Those bugs which fly to secondary host plants, eg nettle, thistle, dock, fat hen and many more, produce offspring that feed on these hosts but later return to strawberries for winter egg laying.

Because of the great agility of capsid bugs it is very difficult to control them by squashing. Any of the sprays already listed will deal with them, applied as soon as they appear in spring. It is most important not to confuse these damaging capsids with the predacious 'black-kneed' species. In fact this is probably mostly found on tree fruits, but we should always keep an eye open for it on strawberries. Its black 'knees' provide certain identifications (see page 72).

EELWORMS

There are three types of damaging eelworms, the Leaf and Bud species, *Aphelenchoides fragariae*, and *A. ritzema-bosi*, and the Stem and Bulb species, *Ditylenchus dipsaci*.

The first two feed on the crowns and young leaves. This produces a puckering and often a failure to expand. Leaflets often show dull silvery feeding areas on the upper surface near the base of the midrib. The main crown ceases to develop, and small secondary crowns appear, giving the plant a typical opened-out appearance. Royal Sovereign in particular may have stunted leaf stalks, often reddish and hairless. A somewhat uncommon side effect is 'cauliflower disease', which is self-explanatory in that the plant assumes a fleshy state with many stunted crown leaves that look something like a cauliflower.

When the stem eelworm is present the leaves become markedly corrugated, and their stems short, thick and distorted. The position regarding this species is complicated by the fact that several races exist, each of which has its particular host or range of hosts other than strawberries, but all of which infest strawberries also. The garden plants most commonly concerned are narcissus, begonia, chrysanthemum, broad beans, parsnip and onions. Strawberries should never follow any of these where infestation has occurred.

Eelworms are extremely difficult to detect by casual observation without a lens. They are thread-like, transluscent and about $\frac{1}{25}$ in long. The Leaf and Bud species lives mainly in leaf axils and amongst the buds of strawberries, and is active at almost any time though mostly in spring.

Eggs are laid in the leaf axils, giving rise to minute larvae, which usually becomes mature in about four weeks.

The Stem eelworm lives and breeds within the plant tissues, and when these have been killed, large numbers of eelworms enter the soil, where they may remain for possibly three years, waiting for the introduction of a suitable host. That is why it is so essential not to plant such hosts in infested land.

It hardly needs saying that runners should never be taken from infested plants, or at least not unless the runners are treated as mentioned below. Complete control of eelworms in the soil is probably outside the gardener's scope, but sterilization with formalin to maker's recommendation will give a fair measure of freedom. Any eelworm residues will however soon lead to populations building up if susceptible plants are put in within two or three years.

Where there is doubt about the infestation of runners, any eelworms on these could be killed by immersing runners in water at a temperature of 115°F for ten minutes against the leaf and bud species, or seven minutes for stem species. It is essential not to exceed ten minutes or the temperature.

There is considerable research in progress into the natural control of eelworms by means of plant root secretions. The plant concerned is the African Marigold and of the species tested, *Tagetes minuta* (which, in spite of its specific name, can reach 10ft in height) appears to be the most effective, having several times the quantity of root secretion that other species have. The theory is that the natural secretions given off by the roots destroy the eelworms' selective mechanism, so that they are unable to determine suitable host plants.

Success with this type of biological control has not so far been spectacular in strawberries, but some success has certainly been claimed. It is worth trying, and those willing to make the trial should contact the Henry Doubleday Research Association for full details. The species of marigold concerned is a half-hardy annual whose foliage is useful for the compost heap towards the end of the season and before frost has killed it.

FLIES

The grub stage of several Crane Flies can cause great damage to strawberry roots. That of the Daddy Longlegs, *Tipula paludosa*, is the worst one, this being the well known leather jacket, the drab coloured, thick skinned grub that reaches about $1\frac{1}{2}$in in length at maturity. Adult flies are often about in large numbers in early autumn. Each female can lay up to 300 black, seed-like eggs in the soil. These hatch in about two weeks and by the following June the grubs are mature, when they become brown chrysalids that work their way slightly above the soil surface just before the flies are due to emerge.

A generally recommended bait is Paris Green but I do not advocate it, since it is poisonous to birds and warm blooded animals, including man. Naphthalene at 2oz per sq yd is useful, also lindane, both for non fruiting beds, or when digging the soil to prepare the bed. Control in fruiting beds is, unfortunately, one of those things one cannot achieve by nonpoisonous or non-tainting methods. All we can do is to get rid of any leather jackets before we plant, and pray that the Daddy Longlegs will give the bed a miss. Grub eating birds are our best allies, and here is a valid argument for not covering the soil with mulch in autumn and winter, since this will make it harder for the birds to find the young grubs.

LEAF HOPPERS

There are some forty species of leaf hoppers occurring on fruit plants. Their status as pests is, in general, hard to determine at present, because adequate research is lacking, but as most cause speckling of the foliage, some physical damage must be caused. At least one of the two strawberry species recorded in the 1950s was found not to transmit crinkle and yellow edge viruses, and it was considered that little harm was caused. Since then, however, certain species belonging to the genera *Aphrodes* and *Euscelis* have been found to transmit another virus from clover to strawberry, namely the Green Petal Disease, and effective control measures will probably have to be evolved. At present all I can suggest is malathion if leaf hopper populations seem to warrant spraying.

These creatures are tiny fly-like insects that sometimes hop off the leaves in clouds when disturbed and fly short distances. This means of course that purely contact sprays are not likely to be very effective, for by the time they have hit the plants the leaf hoppers will have hopped off. For this reason the semi-systemic malathion is preferable, and is in fact known to give good control of hoppers on cane fruits.

MITES

The sap sucking Strawberry Mite, or Tarsonemid Mite, *Steneotarsonemus pallidus*, appears to be chiefly confined to southern England. It is mainly a warm-season pest whose damaging effects are strongly visible by August, though the first signs, difficult to detect, may be found in spring. Mites feed on the unfolded leaflets; these fail to grow and appear brown, wrinkled with down-curled edges. Royal Sovereign is a good indicator. Severely infested plants remain dwarfed, and crop poorly (*see page 72*).

This microscopic species can be made out under a 10x lens, but is almost invisible to the naked eye. It and its eggs will be found along the midrib or anywhere on the surface. The best way to examine a leaflet is to remove it and hold it up to the light. Damage becomes readily apparent as the season advances, and the older leaves assume the typical crinkled look and are brittle to the touch. Small, multiple crowns appear, and runners can be killed quite early.

The mite overwinters as an adult female in the crowns. It becomes active in spring and lays the minute transluscent eggs mainly on the upper surface of young leaflets. There are several generations annually, each overlapping, so that all stages may be present at once. The number of mites on a plant at peak periods has been put at some tens of thousands. Because they object to strong sunlight, they are not found in bright weather in any numbers on exposed areas of the foliage.

Where these mites are identified it is imperative to spray. They cannot possibly be controlled by squashing. Unfortunately, the materials given earlier appear to be of little or no avail. The nearest 'safe' insecticides are nicotine and dicofol. I put the word safe in quotes because although nicotine is a scheduled poison, it is in fact one of the safest in terms of horticultural use, being quick acting and non-residual. Provided the instructions are followed—which almost invariably include a warning not to inhale the fumes and to wash off any deposits on the skin, there will be no danger. A wetter such as soft soap should be included, unless the formulation includes this.

Young plants suspected of carrying mites can be dipped in the correct solution, care being taken to keep the hands free. Plastic gloves are an added insurance. Another method is to immerse the plants for twenty minutes in water at 110°F.

Neither nicotine nor immersion in water is infallible, but both should give a reasonable control. The best time to catch the mites with sprays of either nicotine or dicofol is just after flowering, with perhaps a repeat spray a month later. A post-harvest spray to supplement the earlier ones is sound policy if the summer has been hot and dry.

RED SPIDER MITE

The term 'spider mite' is a contradiction, since mites are not spiders; each belongs to a separate order, but because the sap sucking mites are spider-like in appearance they are referred to as spider mites for the sake of convenience.

That most commonly attacking strawberry is *Tetranychus telarius*, which has a wide host range among plants in the open and under glass. Mites breed in colonies under fine webs on the under-surfaces of the expanded leaves. Their feeding results in greyish or yellowish mottling which spreads as colonies increase. In hot summer the mites can dessicate the foliage of strawberry plants.

The winter is spent in the adult female stage, hibernating quarters being practically anywhere that offers shelter, including the crowns and foliage of the plants. In greenhouses there are often ideal winter quarters, which the mites take full advantage of. They become active in spring and attacks on strawberry plants start then. Eggs are laid on the undersides of the leaves in late April and May, and there are seven or eight generations a year. Dispersal from plants that have been sucked dry to fresh ones is by means of gentle breezes. The mites hang down from the leaves on very fine threads, and are then carried away on the breeze.

Liquid derris or malathion will control this pest in its active stages but will not kill the eggs. It is therefore imperative to spray in early to mid-April before egg laying has started. If attacks went unnoticed then, and do not become visible until eggs have been laid and populations have built up, it will be necessary to apply several sprays at weekly intervals until the infestation has been controlled. Forceful spraying is needed, to penetrate the webs.

MOTHS

The caterpillars of the Ghost Swift Moth, *Hepialus humuli*, and the Garden Swift Moth, *H. lupulinus*, feed on strawberry roots. These are dirty white with a brown head, and dotted with black. The caterpillars spend up to three years in the soil, reaching some $1\frac{1}{2}$in at maturity, when they become brown chrysalids during their final winter. The adult moths are flying in June, when the female drops her eggs on the soil.

These hatch in a week or two and the young caterpillars start to feed. Sometimes the crowns of strawberry plants are eaten.

These caterpillars, again, belong to that unfortunate category which largely defies safe control measures, though lindane or naphthalene, the latter 2oz per sq yd, before planting will effect good control, but as with soil pests in general, digging up is the main approach, together with reliance on birds.

TORTRIX MOTH

The chief diagnostic feature where all fruit tortrix moths are concerned is that the caterpillars spin leaves together, often stuck to the fruit surface. Some other caterpillar species do likewise, but these nearly always grow to a larger size than the tortricids, and do not have the wriggling habit displayed by the latter on disturbance.

The strawberry species, *Argyrotoza comariana* (*see page 89*), hatches in April or May from over-wintered eggs, and feeds on unopened leaves and later on blossom buds. Open flowers are attacked, and these either fail to set, or produce deformed fruits. Leaflets are spun together, or even complete leaves, giving a distinct bunching effect. On the under-leaf surface the caterpillars spin webs, in which they feed and mature. At maturity they are $\frac{1}{4}$in long, green but with a darker coloured back, and the head is shiny yellow with darker marks.

Feeding continues until mid June, when the chrysalis forms in the webbing on the under-leaf surfaces. Moths emerge from late June to late July. The females lay summer eggs, from which the second brood of caterpillars emerges. These are fully grown by September. Finally, these give rise to autumn adults, the females of which deposit the over-wintering eggs.

Post-harvest burning off or cutting off destroys a good many caterpillars of the second generation. The initial attack in spring can be reduced or even eliminated by pyrethrum, but it must be applied before too much leaf spinning has occurred. In practice, the pest is not nearly as serious as this description may seem to imply, and in any case the pest is often almost entirely controlled by its natural parasite in some seasons.

LARGE YELLOW UNDERWING

The caterpillars of this moth, *Triphaena pronuba*, belong in the general class of root feeders. They are dull yellowish, sometimes tinged with green, and have a pale line along each side and along the back. The head is pale brown with darker markings. The moth is on the wing in summer, and sometimes into autumn. The caterpillars live in the soil, feeding on roots from September until May, and they can do a lot of damage to strawberry plants in that time.

Closely allied in habits, though not in species, and feeding from July to September mainly, are the plump greenish brown cutworms, belonging to various species of *Agriotes*. These feed at night.

Light hoeing along the alleyways in runner-free beds is useful as a partial control method for all root eating grubs. As we have seen, we cannot hoe right up to the plants, but the dutch hoe used along the alleys will often turn up grubs, or will be followed quite quickly by grub-taking birds.

SNAILS AND SLUGS

The strawberry has its own snail, *Hygromia striolata*. This is about $\frac{1}{2}$in long, flattish, and varying in colour from reddish brown to grey. In late summer each female lays some sixty eggs. These hatch in autumn, but the young snails lie more or less doggo over winter. In spring they feed on the young leaves and fruit, mainly at night, though warm, wet weather by day will bring them on the feed.

Among slugs, the Garden Slug, *Arion hortensis*, is probably the chief species attacking garden strawberries. It is small, brown, with back and sides marked with dark bands running lengthwise. It is relatively tough skinned, and it leaves a trail of yellow slime.

The Black Slug, *Arion ater*, occupies damp situations, and

may be found tunnelling in the soil as well as on the surface. It has a liking for ripening strawberries. The eggs are transparent, sometimes round, sometimes oval, and the number laid per slug may vary between ten or sixty, always deposited in clusters. Autumn laid eggs may hatch in a few weeks or may remain until spring.

The Field Slug, *Agriolimax reticulatus*, is mottled grey, sometimes with a reddish or yellowish tinge. There are several sub-species of varying colour shades. The bodies of all are very soft.

Chemical slug baits are effective but have a cumulative poison risk for birds and predators. Many people might prefer to lose a few strawberries rather than to lose their resident thrush, and on the basis that food for the soul is more important than food for the body, I am in full agreement. There are quite enough birds killed by farmland chemicals, destruction of habitats and other evils of so-called progressive agriculture. If we are to achieve any compensating balance we must do everything possible to encourage birds in our gardens, and having got them there, we should strive to ensure that they remain.

A safe control of slugs and snails is one part of powdered alum to seven parts of slaked lime, scattered on warm, moist evenings.

WEEVILS

Weevils and beetles are sometimes confused by amateurs, when both types are regarded as beetles. The main diagnostic feature is the proboscis or 'snout' possessed by weevils. This is always present, and in some species is large and plainly seen.

The Blossom Weevil, *Anthonomus rubi*, also known as the Elephant Bug and the Needle Bug, is a black species appearing in April and May. The female punctures the unopened flowers with her snout and then lays eggs in the holes. For some strange reason devised presumably by the good Lord when He made all things great and small, development of the flowers must be prevented if the weevils are to have their day. To ensure this the adult partly or completely severs the bud stalk after laying the egg. When infestation is severe, many buds may be found hanging from partly severed stalks, or lying on the ground when severence has been complete (*see page 90*).

The entire life cycle is spent within the dried up flower bud, which suggests that this creature in its grub stage has solved the problem of living on the bread-line. How it survives on such meagre fare is a mystery, but it does. However, choicer food awaits the adult. This emerges during early July through a hole it makes in the side of the bud. It then feeds on the foliage for a few weeks and finally goes into hibernation until the following spring.

Derris or pyrethrum, applied as soon as the weevils are seen in early May, and repeated ten days later, if they are still evident, should effect control.

The Clay Coloured Weevil, *Otiorrhynchus singularis*, is a strawberry pest mainly in the grub stage. The adult is wingless, brown and lightly speckled, and $\frac{1}{4}$in long. It feeds only at night. Adults emerge from the soil in February. Eggs are laid in summer, and the white, legless grubs feed on strawberry roots until reaching the chrysalis stage in early February. Light cultivation of the ground in February will bring the weevils to the surface, when many will be eaten by birds. Traps of corrugated cardboard laid at evening will entice the weevils. These traps must be collected during the day, when their occupants can be dispatched.

The Fruit Weevil, *Barypithes araneiformis*, bores small holes in the flesh of half grown fruits. These holes have the same characteristics as those made by earwigs in apples; the entrance to each is smaller than the cavity made inside.

The adult is about $\frac{1}{4}$in long, oval, and has a short snout. Its colour varies from shiny black to brown, and pale yellow ones sometimes occur. The grubs live in the soil, feeding on weed roots. Adults are first found on the leaves in late February, when derris will eradicate them.

Perhaps this species does not really deserve a place in the list of major pests, since it is mainly local, but when it does appear it can be abundant and can do considerable damage.

The local name of Elephant Bug for the Blossom Weevil could lead to confusion between this and the locally named Elephant Beetle. It is unfortunate that local names, while often descriptive from the popular point of view, are usually at variance with strict entomology. Thus the Elephant Bug is not a bug as the entomologist recognises the term, and the Elephant Beetle is not a beetle, but is, like the other, a weevil. Its true name is the Strawberry Rhynchites, *Caenorhinus germanicus*. It is about 1/10in long, blue-green, and has a definite snout. With this it punctures the leaves in late March or early April, then turns to the leaf stalks and blossom trusses, from which it bites out small cavities. The female lays up to four eggs in each stalk and then makes several punctures in the stalk just below the eggs. The attacked stalks wilt above the punctures and finally die. Egg laying may go on from mid April to August, but is often completed by late May. This is another fairly local but often damaging pest, frequently most abundant in the vicinity of oak trees, which it also attacks.

When the grubs hatch they feed on the dried up stems, then go to the soil to pupate. The adult stage is reached within a few weeks, but adults remain soil-bound until spring.

To control this pest, apply derris or pyrethrum when the first flower trusses appear, making sure that the spray goes well into the crowns.

It is not only the aerial parts of strawberry plants that are attacked by weevils. Several root feeding types occur in the grub stage, notably the Vine Weevil, *Otiorrhynchus sulcatus*. The adults feed at night on the foliage, and hide by day. These species all occur from about mid April onwards. Eggs are laid in the soil, and the grubs, legless and varying from creamy-white to light brown, have a peculiar shrivelled look and lie curved in the soil, like those of the chafer beetles. They feed on the roots from mid summer until late February, when they pupate (*see page 107*).

Page 125 (above) Strawberry mildew; *(below)* Green Petal
Virus. Note abnormally large sepals and 'seedy' appearance

(left)
Grandee

Page 126

(below)
Elista

Unhappily, these species are very difficult to control. We cannot catch the adults unless we are given to nocturnal prowling, and we can hardly spend hours fiddling around in the soil in search of the grubs. Probably the best method is to try to restrict the grubs by digging up flagging plants complete with soil and grubs, after having made reasonably certain that flagging is not due to drought. Trapping as advised for the Clay Coloured Weevil should secure some adults.

BIRDS

I have already said that birds should be encouraged in the garden, so it may seem strange to include them in the section on pests. I do so only because there is one bird, the linnet, that can assume pest status on strawberries, if it is allowed to. Even so it is not a pest in the wide sense, and to the best of my knowledge is completely harmless where all other fruit are concerned. We cannot deny that some birds destroy buds and flowers on fruits, but the number of species involved is minute, comprising sparrows and bullfinches mainly as bud and blossom takers and blackbirds as soft fruit eaters and robbers of cherries, with tits doing occasional damage to tree fruits. But all these are fairly easily deterred by harmless sprays or by netting.

Linnets, like seed beetles, remove the seeds of strawberries, but there is a distinction between the two types of damage. Beetles take seeds mainly from the undersides of the ripening berries, often leaving a wet wound in the flesh. Linnets generally pick out the seeds cleanly without damaging the flesh, and mostly from the upper sides of the berries.

The damage can be severe; in fact some years ago it was found that linnets were doing more harm in commercial strawberry beds in Kent than beetles were. Linnets are fairly wide-ranging, occurring on heathland, in hedges and in gardens, though I imagine that one of the penalties of living in towns and built up areas is that one seldom sees the birds. Whether one would regard freedom from linnets as a penalty

H

or a blessing depends, I suppose, on one's attitude to life.

Linnet damage is therefore likely to be largely confined to country gardens. The birds do not normally attack green berries. The best preventive is fruit netting. It should not simply be slung over the plants, a method one often sees, but which is never very effective, but should be fixed firmly over battens, so that it is raised clear of the bed. An excellent zinc plated frame, complete with nylon netting and measuring 10ft × 4½ft × 2ft high, has recently appeared, which should give good protection (*see page 107*).

IX

Major Diseases

FUNGUS DISEASES

GREYMOULD (*see page 108*)

We will take the fungus diseases first. Probably the commonest in wet seasons, though it may be absent in dry, is Greymould, *Botrytis cinerea*. This reduces the berries to a grey, furry mess, and can ruin at least a third of the crop in seasons favourable to its spread. Inspection of an infected berry under a lens will reveal short stalks sticking up from the surface and terminating in tiny knobs. These are the spore sacs, which burst open to liberate spores and spread infection. Once infection has struck, affected berries are finished. We cannot cure them, and as they spread the disease by contact as well as by spore liberation, a clean berry in contact with a diseased one will itself become infected. The late Dr Wormald recommended holding the leaves upright by means of rubber bands, and releasing them when the fruit is picked. On small plots this is a useful aid to prevention of greymould, since it facilitates air movement among the plants, which helps to dry out excess moisture.

Host plants of botrytis are legion, and include many weeds. Liberation of spores frequently occurs through physical contact with infected plants, and even the act of pulling up such a plant can cause a shower of spores to be given off if they are ripe. This means that weeds, a potential source of infection, should be kept down.

The strawberries Royal Sovereign, Cambridge Favourite, Talisman, Merton Princess and Cambridge Rearguard are particularly susceptible. In botrytis trials with Talisman in 1966, the percentage of rotted fruit from unsprayed plants was

129

21, and from plants sprayed with thiram it was 4. The weight of sound fruit from 24 unsprayed plants was 32lb, and from 24 sprayed ones it was 38lb.

Prevention of greymould depends basically upon timing of the thiram sprays. Timing is of crucial importance. The first one must go on as the first blossoms open; the second about ten days later, usually at full bloom. When a third spray is necessary, as it may be if the weather is damp at this period, it should be given ten days after the second, when the first fruits are swelling. Infection frequently starts at the calyx; it is therefore essential to wet this adequately.

Thiram is perhaps not the most effective fungicide for botrytis prevention, but it is among the most effective of those available to gardeners. An alternative is captan, almost as effective. Both are liable to cause taint in canned berries and so cannot be recommended unconditionally, but they are quite safe on fruit not destined for canning, and their use at full bloom is not harmful to pollinating insects. A new fungicide based on benomyl was introduced in 1970, after four years' development in the UK. It is for prevention of a range of diseases, including botrytis and mildew on strawberries, and was passed by the Ministry under its approval scheme.

Used in trials on Cambridge Favourite against greymould, this material proved effective.

Wherever mouldy berries are seen they should be removed, preferably before they have shed spores, and burnt. Do not simply throw them down.

It is interesting that air sampling tests at the Long Ashton Research Station, gave a count of 27% more botrytis spores 12in above plants in the open than above those under polythene cloches, possibly owing to the difference in temperature. From 32 unsprayed plants under cloches only 3 infected berries were picked, compared with 135 from the same number of plants in the open.

This suggests that, assuming polythene cloches do not inhibit pollination, their use would be justified as an inhibitor of botrytis, quite apart from any other virtues they may possess. Stagnant air, leading to conditions that delay the drying of berries after rain, always increases the danger of grey-mould, and can be a particular risk where vigorously growing plants are too closely planted, or where too many are jammed into frames and under cloches. Conversely, where there is adequate ventilation, wet berries will dry out more quickly and will be less liable to infection.

LEAF BLOTCH

Strawberry leaves n₁ t infrequently show various spots and blotches that are hard to identify as specific diseases. Nevertheless, they are usually a sign of some fungus trouble. Leaf Blotch, *Zythia fragariae*, occurs first as small brownish spots that later enlarge and have a purplish border surrounded by yellow. The fungal fructifications show up on the discoloured areas as small brownish pimples, often with a pale tip that can be seen through a lens. Spores are given off from these. A further form arises on dead leaf-stalks as black, spherical fructifications with projections that can be seen by the naked eye and look like blackish prickles. This disease flourishes in damp conditions.

LEAF SCORCH

Leaf Scorch, *Diplocarpon earliana*, starts as small dark purplish spots that gradually increase in size to about $\frac{1}{4}$in diameter. They remain dark purplish, with irregular outlines; as the affected area dies, the colour becomes brown. Sometimes there are many spots, when they coalesce to give large areas that finally turn brown, giving the leaf a scorched look. Infected leaves may turn yellow, when the contrasting colours are conspicuous.

The fruiting bodies are shiny black blisters, appearing on the purple areas.

LEAF SPOT

The most common of the leaf spotting fungi is Leaf Spot, *Mycosphaerella fragariae* (*see page 108*). This appears as mainly circular spots about $\frac{1}{8}$in diameter, reddish at first, later whitish with a dark reddish margin. Where infection is moderate the spots are dotted about thinly on the leaves, but where it is severe, the number of spots becomes greatly increased, and leaves may wholly or partly wither. A white mould develops on the spots, leading to the fruiting stage.

This disease, although unsightly, is not as deadly as we may think, though it can certainly be serious in some seasons.

The strawberry leaf spotting fungi have not received much detailed investigation, but standard Bordeaux Mixture given early in the season gives quite good protection, and burning off or cutting off of old foliage after harvest will greatly reduce later infection.

STRAWBERRY MILDEW (see page 125)

Strawberry Mildew, *Sphaerotheca macularis*, is in quite a different class from the leaf spots. It was first recorded in this country in 1854, and now occurs wherever strawberries are grown. Dark blotches appear initially on the upper leaf surfaces, and on the lower there are greyish areas, signifying the presence of the fungus. Later the leaf edges curl upwards, revealing the whitish mildew, and giving a superficial resemblance to drought. The mycelium grows over the lower surfaces, producing many spore-bearing stalks. Spore development and germination are rapid in hot, dry weather; flowers and fruit can be infected as well as leaves. A curious feature of infected flowers is that they sometimes have dark pink petals.

The standard chemical for mildew prevention was for years lime sulphur, and later the milder forms in colloidal and dispersible formulations. These are still good, and relatively cheap, but some people prefer the more expensive dinocap. An advantage of this material is that it is safe on ripening fruits that are to be canned or otherwise processed, whereas sulphur at this stage causes taint. But all sulphur forms are suitable on unripe fruit, or on ripening fruit that is not to be processed. 'Ripening' means the early stage; sulphur is tenacious (but not poisonous) and one must allow time for it to weather away before harvest.

Mildew is prevented by spraying just pre-flower and again at 10–14 day intervals as necessary. Three sprays are usually enough, though four or even five may be needed in a long spell of hot, dry weather.

RED CORE

One of the most serious fungus diseases is Red Core, *Phytopthora fragariae*, a soil inhabiting type that attacks the roots and causes them to rot. This was first recorded in western Scotland in 1921, and for the next fifteen years it wrought havoc there, though it was not recognised in England until 1931. Since then it has spread to all the main strawberry growing districts.

Symptoms first appear in late spring and early summer, when affected plants, often in well defined patches, look as though they are suffering from drought. Growth becomes stunted, leaves are often a dull bluish green, with older ones being sometimes tinged with red, yellow or brown. The plants may flop suddenly, especially in dry weather, and the instinctive reaction of many gardeners would be to apply water. This is somewhat ironic, since the basic condition under which red core flourishes is waterlogging.

The name is derived from the red colour of the core (stele) of the main roots, though occasionally the colour is purplish brown. If the root is sliced lengthwise the red core is plainly seen, or it will be seen in section if the root is cut horizontally.

Section of main root showing red core. Typical 'rat's tail'

The white absorbing rootlets will have mostly rotted away, but a tuft of old, woody rootlets may remain at the tips. The main roots are known as rats' tails, a very apt description. The best time to inspect for the red core is from late autumn until late spring. During summer this symptom is less evident, and all that may show is a general decay of some roots, often with new and apparently healthy growth present. This apparent recovery is a delusion, for as soon as the colder and wetter conditions of autumn and winter set in, the fungus will resume activity and the new roots will be invaded.

We have already seen that roots can be attacked by soil pests, and there are various other causes of rot, but none results in the red core that is typical of this specific disease.

There are two types of spores involved; one type is short lived, occurring on the root surfaces, and being carried by soil water to infect fresh plants; the other type is long lived, and invades the roots. When these have killed the roots they do not die with the rotted root tissues, but remain in the soil. It is not known how long the disease can survive in the absence of new strawberry roots, but the period is at least thirteen years. It is therefore fatal to re-plant into infected land, but as far as is known the disease is specific to strawberries, so infected soil need not be written off.

Red core is introduced almost entirely through planting infected runners, though not quite, for it can also be introduced from infected to non-infected soil on garden tools, which is the soundest argument for emulating the practice of every good gardener of washing tools clean after use. It may be said here that clean tools in the shed mark the best gardeners, dirty ones the worst.

Infected runners, especially when taken in spring for planting, easily go undetected, so the rule is never to propagate from diseased parent plants. Certified stock should always be used; although certification applies to virus diseases, plants grown on land infected with red core, or where the disease has been known to exist, cannot be certified.

No strawberry variety can be guaranteed immune from red core, but Crusader, Talisman, Cambridge Vigour and Rival are probably the most resistant. Redgauntlet, Cambridge Favourite, Prizewinner and Early Cambridge are fairly resistant; Merton Princess, Royal Sovereign and Cambridge Rearguard are the least resistant.

Whatever the degree of resistance, plants will succumb much more readily in wet than in well drained soil. Furthermore, there are several strains of the fungus, some of which are more able to attack strawberry varieties in the high-resistance range than are other strains, and field resistance is complicated by the fact that all strains may occur together.

Freedom from wet soil is imperative, and this is where the previously mentioned ridge culture is a valuable technique. Even where the soil is too wet for surface culture, strawberries can still be grown on ridges. An extension of the method is to lay polythene strips over the ridge tops before planting, with their sides turned into the ridge flanks or fixed along the base with stones. These prevent flooding by rain and allow excess water to drain off into the alleys.

Cross cuts are made at planting positions, the flaps lifted and the plants set. Flaps must be left up and the holes must be large enough to allow adequate penetration by rain or hand watering. Runner production is ruled out while the strips remain, but where home propagation is wanted the strips can be removed.

Every effort should be made to keep the alleyways reasonably drained, and provided this is achieved, catch cropping of lettuces and other suitable subjects can be undertaken.

VERTICILLIUM WILT

One of the strongest arguments in favour of rotating strawberries is that rotation offers a good safeguard against Verticillium Wilt. There are several species of this fungus; the two that mostly attack strawberries are *Verticillium albo-atrum* and *V. dahliae*. They all have a fairly wide host range; as the specific name of the second mentioned implies, dahlias are an alternative host. Others are potatoes, tomatoes and the common weeds groundsel, thistles and plantains.

These fungi are soil inhabiting and invade stems and crowns, especially of maiden plants. Older plants are less susceptible. Older leaves wilt, and the fruit on infected plants is small and often malformed. Bluish-black streaks extend from the crown along the stalks of wilting leaves. The latter turn brown, and usually the plant dies. If an affected crown is cut across it will often show a brown discolouration of the tissues.

One of the best indicators of this disease is the potato, but unfortunately gardeners do not always recognise it, mainly because the yield of lightly infected plants is not greatly reduced. It might be as well therefore if we consider the symptoms on potato.

Leaflets become severely rolled and cupped and hang down, and always from the shoot top downwards. Wilt is rather a mis-nomer, because the foliage remains firm, until drying up occurs, which starts at the base and works upwards. The woody tissues in the stem will show a yellowish-brown colour. Tubers do not show any signs of disease, though in fact they are infected, and any that are used for planting will perpetuate the disease. After the plant dies the fungus passes into all the dead tissues, and remains there until the following season, which means that scraps of dead plants left in the soil, or haulms that are dug in, are sources of future infection, so that strawberries planted into the vacant land will almost certainly become infected in some degree.

Thus we see that although rotation is essential in the interest of freedom from disease in general, it can be fatal to strawberries if they follow plants that were attacked by a disease that attacks strawberries as well.

It is unfortunate that wilt resistance has played no part in strawberry breeding in the past, though it probably will in the future. However, trials have been made to try to establish degrees of resistance, or at least of tolerance, the latter being the term used to denote that a variety will crop in varying amounts even when infected. The land chosen was heavily contaminated from potatoes in 1959 and was cropped almost continuously with strawberries from 1960 to 1967.

We need not go fully into the data; a short summary will

suffice. Of some of the varieties most likely to be planted by gardeners, Templar, Crusader and Prizewinner suffered an average of over 80% infection; Cambridge Vigour 70%; Merton Herald and Gorella 45%; Redgauntlet and Talisman 15%. The lowest figures recorded were 6.5% for Cambridge Favourite; 4.5% for Merton Princess; 2.5% for Cambridge Premier; 2% for Talisman and 1.5% for Royal Sovereign.

It was concluded that if there was no alternative to planting on infected land, then Cambridge Favourite, Premier, Merton Princess, Redgauntlet and Sovereign would be the least likely to suffer. This is worth bearing in mind, but it does not alter the fact that planting into infected soil is a most perilous procedure, and is bound to perpetuate the fungus in some degree. The survival period for verticillium wilt in the soil is not known, but it is thought that the period may be many years, even in the absence of host plants.

There are two chemicals used as soil fumigants. One is chloropicrin, which is not available to gardeners, and is a high risk chemical demanding specialised application; the other is metham-sodium, which is available to gardeners. This is watered on to the soil, and the soil is then covered with sacking for a few days. No planting must be done for at least ten weeks.

Metham-sodium is much less of a risk than chloropicrin, but is not completely safe, and must not come into contact with eyes and skin. It gives a fairly high rate of control, but probably not a complete kill of the fungus. I do not advocate its use, since I try to exclude all poison risk, but in small gardens where there is danger of verticillium becoming strongly established because of insufficient space for the exclusion of all wilt susceptible subjects, there may be no alternative to fumigation. Metham-sodium is highly damaging to plants and must never be allowed to drift.

The reaction of strawberries to wilt disease can be variable. For example, when five isolates from four strawberry varieties in widely separated localities were inoculated into Cambridge Favourite, two isolates gave a high incidence of wilt, but the remainder gave a lower incidence. This showed that even the normally fairly safe Favourite can be acutely infected if it is attacked by a particularly virulent strain.

Another example of variation in susceptibility was provided by Cambridge Premier. The low incidence mentioned above was related to trials in Kent; the same variety tested at Long Ashton, near Bristol, proved very susceptible.

We can say that virtually no British variety is immune, and that infection will vary according to virulence of fungal strain and local conditions. There are far less data on the latest continental varieties. These are sometimes advertised as showing no signs of disease, which may be perfectly true as far as their nursery condition is concerned, but it does not necessarily mean that no diseases will attack them in the garden. In fact certain forms of infection have been noticed in one or two of the new varieties. Efficient weed control to eliminate wild hosts of verticillium wilt has been shown to reduce infection in strawberries. In September 1969 the incidence of the disease on herbicide treated as against cultivated plots showed a reduction from approximately 30% to 6% on Cambridge Favourite, and from approximately 57% to 36% on Cambridge Vigour. Thus, even with herbicides infection was not eliminated, but the results do suggest that if weed seedlings are destroyed early with simazine, the danger will at least be lessened on suspected land, and where the gardener does not want to fumigate.

The fact that the infection figure for Cambridge Favourite on the cultivated plot was nearly five times greater than that for this variety on the heavily contaminated potato land (6.5%) does not necessarily invalidate the latter result, or the conclusion from it that Favourite would be among the least likely to suffer if planted on infected land. Nor need the difference between the two values for Cambridge Vigour, ie 57% on cultivated versus herbicide plot as against 70% on the potato land, cause undue speculation. Such variations are quite common in experimental work and reflect differing conditions that frequently arise between regions, relating to soil, climate and other factors. They do undoubtedly appear confusing and even contradictory, but we must remember that any definite advice emanating from trials, as distinct from tentative advice, is based on a full assessment of related work. The results are co-ordinated and the conclusions drawn from the whole.

Where the final conclusion leaves some marked discrepancy, this is usually recorded; for example, Cambridge Premier, as we have seen, reached a figure of only 2.5% wilt infection in Kent, but reached a high figure near Bristol. One would therefore be justified in planting this in south-east England, but in the south-west it could prove highly susceptible.

The systemic fungicide based on benomyl, which I mentioned under Greymould, has given good trial results against verticillium wilt in Cambridge Vigour. Used as a soil drench, and applied three times, it gave complete control of plants previously inoculated with the disease, when used at the highest of three concentrations, ie 0.2%. At a concentration of 0.05% it gave 85–100% control, while the lowest concentration of 0.0125% reduced the initial infection to 96%, but failed to sustain this level, and infection finally reached 52%.

Such figures are not of much practical interest to amateurs, because by the time a new material has been released for general use, the optimum concentration of active ingredient is decided and is automatically included in the formula, and all that the user has to do is to apply the recommended dilution. Nevertheless, it is worth having such data, if only to be assured that spray materials do not contain more active ingredient than is necessary.

The same experiments were made with potted plants of Cambridge Vigour. There was a gap of eight weeks after inoculation, by which time the plants were severely wilted, until the treatment was applied. Symptoms diminished soon after the first application, and good control was achieved during the season.

VIRUS DISEASES

CRINKLE AND YELLOW EDGE

The classic virus diseases of strawberries are Crinkle and Yellow Edge. Crinkle was first recorded in Great Britain in 1933 on Royal Sovereign. There are two forms, mild and severe. Mild Crinkle or Mottle, shows as tiny, scattered, yellowish spots on the leaves. In time the spots develop a reddish or purplish centre. These symptoms are very hard to diagnose with certainty, except by a specialist, and it is possible that thousands of garden plants of Sovereign become infected. Cropping is not greatly reduced and plants usually survive throughout their normal span.

Severe Crinkle is much more serious. Here the spots are usually more numerous, and the leaf cells at the spotted areas fail to grow. The rest of the leaf does continue to grow, with the result that marked distortion or crinkling occurs, often with a distinct red colour appearing. Leaf stalks remain normal in length, so that the plant is not dwarfed or flattened. A few varieties, of which Huxley is an example, are symptomless carriers. These may fail to fruit, or may produce poor crops for no very evident reason. Plants infected with severe crinkle will soon become more or less worthless.

Yellow edge is seen most clearly in late summer and autumn. Young crown leaves are the first to show the disease. Their edges assume a yellow, indistinct line that merges into the green area. This leads to diminished growth, with the leaf margins often cupping. Leaf stalks also cease to grow, and the plants become markedly dwarfed and flattened. On Royal Sovereign the natural red colour of the leaf stalks is missing; the stalks, though short, are not reduced in girth, but are stouter than normal. The vectors of yellow edge and crinkle are aphids.

ARABIS MOSAIC

A virus disease that has become prominent in recent years is Arabis Mosaic. This causes yellow blotches on the leaves of

Royal Sovereign, sometimes slight, sometimes very marked, according to the strain of the virus. Cambridge Favourites and Cambridge Prizewinner often show severe symptoms, and all three of these varieties can be severely stunted when infected by the most virulent strain. Symptoms vary between varieties and it is not always easy to diagnose mosaic with certainty. The basic pattern is, however, a 'mosaic' of yellow, quite distinct from the merging yellow margin of yellow edge, and whereas some crinkling and distortion may occur, as in severe crinkle, the distinguishing feature between the two is the mosaic pattern, this being present in arabis mosaic, but absent in crinkle.

Arabis mosaic is spread through the soil by a species of Dagger Nematode (or eelworm) known as *Xiphinema diversicaudatum*. This infests certain weeds and hedgerow trees, and is nearly always more abundant in the vicinity of hedges. How far it can travel in the soil is not known, but the standard recommendation is to leave a wide margin between a hedge and the strawberry bed. I hope this will not be taken by anyone as an excuse for grubbing out hedges. It may be said with fair certainty that the value of hedges far outweighs their possible danger as haunts of eelworms.

GREEN PETAL (*see page 125*)

During the last few years I have received a number of samples from gardeners of strawberry plants with small, cupped, green petals and very large sepals. These have been infected by the Green Petal virus. Fruit on such plants is 'seedy' and shrivels, and foliage is olive-green with older leaves turning red in summer. During late summer or sometimes earlier, there is usually a sudden wilting of the leaves, often followed by a few small, yellowish ones.

Often the plant collapses in summer and dies. The presence of the small yellowish leaves, shivelled fruits and dried inflorescences distinguishes this disease from verticillium wilt, and the sudden collapse as distinct from stunting but without collapse, distinguishes it from other virus diseases.

For many years green petal was confused with wilt, and it was not until 1951, when Climax became widely planted, that a clear distinction was observed, since this variety showed definite petal symptoms much more clearly than previous varieties had. On Royal Sovereign, for example, flower symptoms are less marked, and here one must look for the new growth of small, yellow leaves and reddening of the old foliage.

There are at least two viruses involved, and a number of variants, differing in virulence. One causes a leaf bronzing and wilt, but without green petals. This form of infection has been attributed to green petal in the past; the lack of definite petal symptoms has been explained as being due to infection having taken place too late for the petals to be affected. This form is now considered to be distinct, and to be caused by one of the two known viruses, ie the Witch's Broom virus of clover. Green petal is caused by the other one, namely the Phyllody virus of clover.

Both viruses have numerous host plants apart from strawberry, eg cereals, red clover, helenium, carrot, celery, mayweed and pimpernel.

The vectors are certain species of leaf hoppers belonging mainly to the genera *Aphrodes* and *Euscelis*. A noticeable feature of the movement of these vectors from wild hosts to strawberries has been that such movement is much less marked in cool wet summers, when growth of the primary and preferred wild host plants is good. In 1955 the autumn was dry, and the following spring green petal was very high in strawberries, suggesting that virus-carrying leaf hoppers had abandoned the relatively dry wild plants, which offered little in the way of the sap on which the insects feed, and had flown to irrigated strawberries. In a field in Sussex about a third of an acre of Sovereign became infected. The plants in one part of the field had been irrigated the previous autumn after planting, but the rest of the acreage had not. The rate of infection in the irrigated area was nearly twice that in the non-irrigated.

(right)
Gento

(left)
Triscana

Page 144

(right)
Frapendula

Normally the incidence of green petal and its related form is only about $3\frac{1}{2}\%$ annually in commercial strawberry growing, and should be very low in gardens where clover and the other wild hosts are absent. Town gardeners may never see it.

Since the main migration from wild plants to strawberries occurs in dry weather, rural gardeners in particular should be on the lookout for leaf hoppers in drought periods, and should apply malathion if any are seen among the strawberries.

The exact relationship between strawberries and wild hosts is perhaps not fully resolved where all leaf hopper species are concerned, but it is known that several cannot transmit the disease from wild plants to strawberries, but can transmit it from strawberries to wild plants, and also from one type of weed to another. These leaf hopper species therefore establish a 'supply' of the virus among the wild host range, which is tapped by the species that spread it from the weeds to strawberries.

When a leaf hopper feeds on an infected plant—even if only for a few minutes—it imbibes infection, but before it can transmit this there must be a period of latency, which may be of several weeks. The virus does not vanish from the insect, however, but becomes active when the latent period has ended, and the leaf hopper remains capable of transmission for the rest of its life.

Once a virus invades the gardener's strawberry plants, they will in most instances degenerate quite rapidly. There is no cure, and since an infected plant is a source of further infection, it should be destroyed. The aim must be to prevent the insect vectors from claiming tenants' rights. This is certainly easier in theory than in practice, for it demands a vigilance that perhaps only the strong-minded or the dedicated possess. However, as I have indicated, viruses are appreciably less of a menace than they were, and a combination of reasonable control of the vectors, together with a two or three-yearly re-planting programme, should ensure freedom from virus diseases, particularly if certified plants are bought.

In practically every example of virus infection I have seen

J

in garden strawberries, either the plants were aged, and should have been grubbed long before, or else no attempt at sensible pest control had been made. In fact, I usually found these two went together.

This brings us to the end of the major pests and diseases. It may seem a formidable list, and long as it is, it is not complete, for I have omitted lesser enemies. But at the risk of repetition I would say again that pest and disease control can be reduced to a comparatively simple and painless exercise, if one takes the trouble to learn about the essentials of symptoms and life histories. Without this knowledge, or with only a smattering of it, which is the greater of the two evils, we shall either spray when we need not, or we shall not spray when we should. And even if we never come up against some of the troubles mentioned, it is as well to know that they exist.

PART IV

X
Varieties

Although Royal Sovereign remains in the estimation of many people the finest strawberry grown, at least among the summer fruiters, it has definite snags. The main ones are its susceptibility to virus infection and the fact that it demands growing conditions above those tolerated by lesser varieties, plus a generally fairly exacting standard of culture. Furthermore it is seldom a heavy cropper as we understand the term today. I was almost tempted to omit it from my list, but have included it because there must be gardeners who are prepared to meet its needs to the best of their ability and to accept its somewhat erratic cropping.

There is some evidence of duplication of the main qualities among some of the latest introductions; the chief merit of these is that they offer alternatives. We will begin with the British summer fruiting kinds, in order of ripening. These are largely dominated by the Cambridge series raised by Mr D. Boyes. Where I have mentioned susceptibility to a disease, this is not meant to imply that the variety should necessarily be passed over, but simply that such susceptibility should be borne in mind, and a watch kept for the possible appearance of the disease if the variety is planted. Reference back to the earlier notes on varietal responses to diseases should, I hope, be of some additional interest.

CAMBRIDGE VIGOUR
(first early from maiden plants, but older plants crop later)

Plant large, upright, spreading. Flowers well protected. Fruit fairly large, but losing size later, conical, orange red, later becoming scarlet. Firm, juicy flesh, fairly sweet, good flavour. A fairly heavy cropper, outstanding in first year.

Mainly resistant to red core, very susceptible to wilt and sensitive to drought. Susceptible to botrytis. It is good for cloche work and deep freezing and is an excellent choice for those who want a worthwhile return from plants cropped for one season and then scrapped. Its first big, wedge shaped berries are a joy for early season tea parties, and the smaller ones that follow can be used for jam.

CAMBRIDGE RIVAL (early to second early)

Plant tall, fairly open, fairly vigorous. Flowers protected. Fruits large at first, later medium-large or smaller, conical, bright crimson, darker when ripe. Flesh fairly firm, pale scarlet, flavour excellent. This is perhaps the best flavoured of the earlier season Cambridge series. Suitable for forcing. Needs careful handling; bruises easily. Susceptible to wilt.

CAMBRIDGE FAVOURITE (second early to mid-season)

Plant fairly large and open, vigorous. Flowers mainly protected. Fruit large, maintaining size, pinkish scarlet, turning light red. Firm, fairly juicy flesh, deep salmon pink to pale red. Moderate flavour. Crops well in the open, under cloches and in frames. Fairly resistant to mildew, subject to green petal. This is probably the commonest variety in its season, freely available in the shops, when its flavour is only moderate and sometimes poor. Garden grown, and fresh picked, it can reach a better standard, but hardly warrants preferential place.

CAMBRIDGE LATE PINE (late)

Plant vigorous, fairly open. Flowers well protected. Fruit medium to large, rounded, crimson. Flesh firm, very sweet, giving excellent flavour. Crops heavily and is first rate for processing. Said to be resistant to mildew. An outstanding late berry.

This list does not exhaust the Cambridge series, but comprises all that the gardener in search of the best need consider. It will be seen that a factor common to all is that the flowers are protected by the foliage. This is an excellent characteristic, often lessening appreciably the danger of frosted blossoms, but it can encourage botrytis in wet seasons, by reducing air circulation. Even where this disease is not mentioned in my list we should be on guard in wet seasons.

CRUSADER

Raiser, R. D. Reid, Scottish Horticultural Research Institute. Plant medium large. Flowers carried on long, spreading trusses not well protected. Fruit medium size, well shaped, bright red becoming darker. Flesh firm, of rich flavour. High resistant to red core.

MERTON HERALD

Raiser, John Innes, Horticultural Institute. Plant medium, open. Flowers not well protected. Fruit fairly large, conical, light orange-red. Flavour excellent.

ROYAL SOVEREIGN (mid-season)

Raiser, Laxton Bros. Bedford. Introduced in 1892. Plant medium large, rather open, moderately vigorous. Flowers partly protected, but in general susceptible to frost. Fruit medium to large, roundish, conical, scarlet when ripe. Flesh fairly firm, juicy, salmon pink or pale red. Flavour sweet, subacid, first rate. Moderate cropper in general, but can yield heavily under good conditions. Generally regarded as the King of British summer fruiting strawberries. Very susceptible to virus and fungus troubles and demands a high standard of culture. It cannot be recommended universally, any more than Cox's Orange apple or Comice pear, and even the finest strain skilfully grown can be disappointing in yields. Nevertheless, its quality is superior to most other varieties. On the show bench other strawberries may possess glamour, but the very name Royal Sovereign has a kind of magic, and it is probably true to say that a gardener's skill in strawberry growing will be reflected pre-eminently in an exhibit of perfect examples of this variety.

REDGAUNTLET (mid to mid late)

Raiser, R. D. Reid. Plant medium large, fairly open, upright and spreading, vigorous. Flowers partly protected. Fruit large to very large, scarlet becoming dark crimson. Flesh firm, fairly juicy, deep scarlet. Flavour fair, when berries are properly ripe, but poor if berries picked too soon and ripened indoors. Heavy cropper, maintaining size. Autumn crop follows if old leaves are cut off immediately after summer harvest and plants cloched in September, but the heaviest autumn crops might be had by not mowing at all and by September cloching, a point which experimental gardeners should bear in mind.

TALISMAN (mid season to late)

Raiser, R. D. Reid. Plant medium, upright, dense, fairly vigorous. Growth is slow at first. Flowers fairly protected. Fruit medium-large at first, but smaller later, reddish-orange, turning dark scarlet. Flesh firm, juicy, scarlet. Flavour good. Crops well, and may give an autumn yield of fairly small berries. Largely resistant to red core and mildew. Good for forcing. Mr Reid recommends the removal of all runners, to prevent the beds from becoming matted, which can result in small fruits liable to botrytis. He states that it is advisable to cut down foliage immediately after fruiting. This benefits the following season's crop. Planting should be wider than with most varieties since this one carries more crowns and flower buds than most, and needs more space. It is a better variety than many for retaining into its second cropping year, especially in conditions where the maiden crop is somewhat under the optimum, and is a good choice for gardeners whose time is limited, provided they spend their limited time in removing the rampaging runners.

CONTINENTAL VARIETIES

The main feature of some, though not all, of the continental introductions, especially those from Germany, bred by Herr Hummell, is their enormous size. Mere size in a strawberry is not enough; it must combine with good flavour.

The continental varieties are divided into summer fruiters, mainly June to July, and 'Perpetual' types fruiting from June to October, usually with the heaviest crop in autumn. At present they are virtually disease free, though research work suggests that this does not necessarily mean that all are disease resistant. They are, however, not at all demanding, in spite of their exotic appearance. The primary need is adequate root moisture to enable the berries to reach their true size. Mr Ken Muir, who is a main supplier of these plants, puts their water needs plainly. 'Once plants are established, further watering should be unnecessary, except during very dry periods after petal fall, when the soil should be soaked thoroughly every 4–5 days.' To obtain the best from the continental varieties, gardeners should make sure they receive Mr Muir's leaflet, which sets out the main cultural points with admirable clarity.

THE SUMMER FRUITERS

PRECOSA (very early)

This is not a giant, but is of medium size. Cropping is moderate, but flavour is excellent, and the variety deserves first place in the garden, since flavour is superior to that of Cambridge Vigour.

PRECOSANA (early)

This is similar in size and crop to Precosa, and almost as well flavoured. In trials at the Efford Experimental Station it managed a nicely balanced size grade throughout its season, producing 30% large berries from 25 May to 5 June, 23% from 6–12 June and 20% from 13–25 June.

GRANDEE (early) (see page 126)

Produces giant sized berries up to 3in in diameter and 3oz in weight. Well flavoured and a heavy cropper, especially in its second year.

BEMANIL (mid-season)

Medium sized fruits, and medium cropping. Particularly recommended for jam.

ELISTA (mid-season to late) (*see page* ??)

A Dutch variety making medium sized friuts that are specially suitable for processing and deep freezing. Flowers late and is virtually frost free. Makes very compact growth, and plants may be set at 9in apart. Ideal for container growing. Heavy cropper. This variety is of special value in small gardens. It is another of the comparatively few continentals to date to have been independently assessed. At Efford it produced 46.3% large berries and 25.6% medium sized from 25 May to 5 June. From 6–12 June the respective figures were 30.5 and 30.3%. From 13–25 June they were 25.5 and 26.6%. It was rated as a somewhat dark coloured fruit lacking in flavour, whereas its introducer rates it as having a distinctive strawberry taste, ideal for dessert, and excellent for processing, jam and deep freezing.

FANIL (mid-season) (*see page 143*)

Giant size, in the Grandee class. A Belgian variety raised at the State Research Station in 1961. Some berries are 'fan shaped', and are probably unique in this respect. Colour is described as cardinal-red, flavour excellent. Fills the gap between Grandee and the full cropping season of the perpetuals.

GORELLA

This is another newcomer about which we have some details from Efford. It is a well flavoured berry, though it produced appreciably less crop than Elista, but just over half the total berries were graded large, of which 80% was picked by 5 June. Certain virus-like symptoms have been found in runner beds, and are under investigation.

GIGANA (mid-season)

Berries large and firm, not quite so large as Grandee. Good

flavour and cropping power. The same virus-like symptoms as above have been found.

SENGANA (mid-season)

A well flavoured, darkish red berry that has the virtue of retaining its colour when processed.

DOMANIL (late)

Another Belgian variety, bearing good crops of medium-large, well flavoured berries.

PERPETUALS

GENTO (*see page 143*)

This German variety is the star of the recently introduced perpetuals. It fruits almost continuously from June to early October on parent plant and runners. Berries are large, wedge shaped, bright crimson and possess fine flavour. It won a Gold Medal at Karlsruhe in 1967.

TRISCANA (*see page 144*)

This also crops from June to October, bearing very large fruits, firm, dark red and very sweet.

FRAPENDULA (*see page 144*)

Ideal for window boxes, tubs and containers generally. It fruits freely on parent plant and runners, and is exceedingly decorative when grown in hanging baskets and similar containers. This is an ideal example of a heavily cropping strawberry that takes up little space, and so should appeal to everyone whose facilities are limited. It is officially termed autumn fruiting, because the largest yield comes in autumn, but as it starts to fruit in June, we can include it under the perpetuals.

REMONT

This is another heavy cropper producing medium sized, well flavoured berries from June to October.

TRIPLEX

This also gives its largest crop in autumn. The berries are large, of good flavour, and so far appear to be resistant to botrytis.

In case it should be thought that the modern perpetuals represent the only noteworthy ones in the category, I would point out that the older French types—Sans Rivale and St Claude, and the French derived Hampshire Maid, are first rate strawberries. St Claude in particular, deserves special mention. It makes a neat plant with well shaped dark red berries of a richness that is perhaps unsurpassed by any recent introduction, and it seems to have withstood disease remarkably well. The main efforts of breeders of the new perpetuals seem to have been directed towards increasing the cropping power by inducing runner fruiting in addition to the fruiting of the main plant, together with increase in berry size. Their results have been very successful, but when size and quantity are the criteria, quality often suffers, and my own belief is that the fine flavour of the best perpetuals in the older range has not been passed on to the new varieties. It is a matter of the difference between a mass standard, universally accepted as good, and the extra standard demanded by the epicure. St Claude is an epicurean fruit, in the class that puts a superlative wine above even the best of the common run. Perpetuals are, in general, more sun loving than shorter season types, and prefer an open site rather than semi-shade.

At this point a final brief mention may be made of the varietal trials at Efford. Montrose was outstanding among the new varieties with 60% of its total in the large grade, of which nearly 47% was picked from 25 May to 5 June. The heaviest marketable cropper was Elista, followed by another new one, Merton Dawn, then by Montrose, Gorella and Redgauntlet. All data were for the period 25 May to 25 June. Maiden plants were set on 29 August and lightly irrigated. Tunnel cloches were placed over the plants on 18 February. Although Redgauntlet produced very well (6.3 tons per acre with 43% in the large grade, of which 70% was picked by 5 June) it was considered to have fallen well behind the other varieties when fruit size distribution over the main market periods, and total yield, were considered.

We must of course appreciate that the trial was essentially for market growers; although a variety that gives its highest percentage of large berries early in the season, like Gorella, is best for commercial growers, the same does not necessarily apply to gardeners, who are not selling their fruit, but would no doubt prefer large berries to be spread more evenly over a variety's entire season, as was the case with Precosana.

Some stocks of Merton Dawn have been found to be infected with a virus known as vein chlorosis.

ALPINES

Today the alpines have been virtually reduced to one variety, Baron Solemacher. It may not be the best ever produced, but it is undoubtedly an exceptionally fine berry and is without question a fruit for the connoisseur. It produces over an extended season and the berries make jam of a quality that is far above that of the conventional kinds, and with which shop bought strawberry jam bears no comparison. One reason may be that, being rich in pectin, the fruit needs nothing to make the jam set. Only God, who sees all, and the jam makers know what goes into mass produced jam to achieve this purpose.

STRAWBERRIES ON TRELLIS

The ability of some modern perpetuals to fruit on runners has led not only to the introduction of varieties that will produce from trailing runners but also to some that can have these led upwards and tied to trellis work and other forms of support. Obviously there must be not only the fruiting ability but also the growth properties necessary to ensure that the runners will keep growing.

The most notable example seems to be Skyscraper. It is claimed that this produces fruiting runners profusely up to a height of five to six feet, in addition to the crop given from the parent plant, and that its perpetual nature enables it to go on cropping 'for years and years'. How many years are not specified.

It is planted in early spring, and starts to crop by about June. It then continues until frost cuts the flowers. The decorative value of a strawberry plant having this nature of growth and cropping is obvious. The planting area is given as 2sq ft per plant.

XI

Pollination and Fertilisation

Before flowers can turn into fruit two distinct processes are necessary. First, he pollen contained in the anthers must be transferred to the stigmas; then the pollen grains must grow by sending out a tube downwards inside the 'stalk' of the stigma (the style) and must produce certain substances that unite with the egg cells to effect their fertilisation within the ovary.

Ripe stigmas, ready to receive pollen grains, excrete a sticky substance which not only secures the pollen grains but also feeds them. Since they are living entities, capable of growth, they must receive nourishment before growth can proceed. When the egg cells have been fertilised they become seeds; these grow, together with the surrounding ovary which, in many plants, becomes the fruit.

As we have seen earlier, the fruit of the strawberry are the small, seed-like achenes embedded in the surface of the receptacle, and in their case fertilisation leads to swelling not of the ovaries (or not beyond the seed-like stage) but to the receptacle, which becomes the edible portion.

Some fruits, or their varieties, are termed self-compatible, others self-incompatible. The former will set fruit with their own pollen, the latter will not, but must receive pollen from a different variety of their kind. A notable example is the Cox's Orange Pippin apple, which must be cross-pollinated with pollen of a different variety of apple. (Cross-pollination between different species is no good; thus, for example, plum pollen will not pollinate apples, nor will the reverse succeed.)

There are certain incompatible types of strawberry, but they have been virtually eliminated from general cultivation, and there is no need to plant more than one variety simply to provide for pollination. However, strawberry flowers are not as accommodating as we would wish. Theoretically, full pollination cannot be effected unless ripeness and dispersal of pollen coincide with stigma receptivity. Unfortunately they do not always coincide among strawberry flowers, which means that on any particular cluster there may be some flowers whose anthers and stigmas are not 'paired'. In this event pollen will fall on to unripe stigmas and will die; alternatively, stigmas may be ahead of anther splitting, waiting in vain for pollen, and by the time this appears the stigmas may prove no longer receptive.

Apart from this lack of co-operation, other factors like cold wind or excessive moisture may intervene, in the first case to shrivel pollen grains and floral organs, in the second to inhibit pollen dispersal, since pollen grains must be dry if they are to be effectively transferred to stigmas.

Thus there are several hazards between pollination and fertilisation. As far as pollen transference in relation to the coincidence, or its lack, of anther splitting and stigma ripeness is concerned, the problem is to some extent theoretical on strawberries because it is usually overcome successfully in fine weather, though not always in poor, by pollinating insects, provided these are given full access to the flowers. Their constant forays ensure that the majority of blossoms are adequately pollinated, because even where some anthers and stigmas on particular trusses do not coincide for pollen transference, ripe stigmas will receive pollen from other trusses.

The other possible agent in pollination is wind, but it would be far too optimistic to rely on this entirely. For one thing the efficiency of wind as a pollinating agent is a doubtful matter, and for another, there may not be much movement at just above ground level anyway.

The necessity for providing free access to flying insects cannot be too strongly emphasised, and has particular relevance to forced plants. Daily removal of alternate cloches, or perhaps more than alternate ones, and opening of greenhouse lights and doors throughout the flowering season, and the avoidance of netting until after fruit set are measures that will encourage maximum insect activity among the blossoms.

BERRY MALFORMATION

It is not uncommon to find some malformed berries at harvest, especially on plants under long rows of cloches. In some instances this is combined with initial malformation of the flowers, particularly the earliest opening ones. At East Malling on 8 May 1959, when 60% of the flowers of one-year-old Redgauntlet were open, 94% of them had malformed stamens; on the same date, 15% of the flowers of two-year plants were open, all of which showed malformed stamens. This variety had 66% of flowers on two-year plants open on 14 May, of which 91% were malformed, and on 27 May 87% of flowers were open, of which 80% were malformed. At picking time 38% of Redgauntlet berries were malformed in varying degrees, but only 10% in Sovereign. There was an interesting example of the fact that although faulty seed development in an isolated area of a berry will result in distortion of the receptacle in that area, such distortion does not necessarily occur if poorly developed seeds are distributed evenly over the surface. A Redgauntlet berry with 232 seeds had only 86 that were fully developed; yet the berry was perfect in shape.

The second flowering of the Redgauntlets, ie in autumn, produced only 30% of perfect flowers, and their fruits were subsequently considerably malformed. The type of berry distortion on the crop from the spring flowers was distinctly different from that on the autumn crop. The former took no clearly defined form, but showed a variety of dents, protuberances and carbuncular effects, while the latter was mainly confined to the berry tip, resulting in a pointed or a flattened knob.

Another variety that has exhibited various forms of distortion is Cambridge Prizewinner.

In 1967 further observations revealed that malformation

K

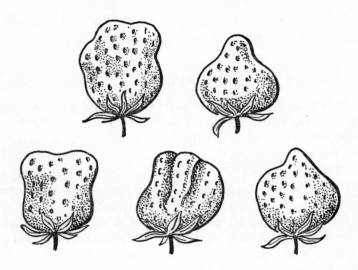

Malformation due to imperfect pollination

declined in the season, but in Redgauntlet the final figure was still half that recorded from the first crop given by the early flowers, as it was in a count made in 1961. This variety together with Cambridge Rival and Merton Herald gave the highest incidence among ten varieties, and Templar and Talisman the least.

Cambridge Rival had 58% severely malformed fruits at the first pick, Redgauntlet 51%, and the respective figures for perfect berries were 7% and 24%. The intermediate values, ie 35% and 25%, were made up of slightly malformed fruit.

Among unpicked plants in another plot there were severely malformed fruits and examples of complete failure of receptacles to swell.

A possible cause of berry malformation is frost damage to the berries. Frosted blossoms do not set, but in some seasons a late May frost can kill the seeds on the exposed side of the berry. The effect is virtually the same as that caused by other forms of seed damage resulting in the death of seeds, when berries are young, namely a cessation of receptacle growth at the affected spot. This inevitably means berry distortion in some degree.

This damage is well known, but where berry malformation occurs in the absence of frost, some other factor must be sought, and the indications are that ineffective pollination may be the cause. This can arise for a number of reasons; pollen may be of poor quality, with a low viability; temperature and atmospheric conditions may be unsuitable for pollen dissemination or growth of tubes; or fertilisation of the ovules may be inadequate.

Any of these factors, or some or all of them combined, could mean that only a proportion of strong seeds will form, in which event those areas of berries bereft of good seeds will become distorted.

Some of these factors are genetical and so outside the gardener's control, but as berry malformation is nearly always more pronounced in degree and quantity under cloches than in the open, it is not unreasonable to suppose that, genetics and weather conditions apart, the most likely cause is inadequate transfer of pollen from anthers to stigmas because of a lack of insects to carry out this indispensable transference. Here it may be said that some self-pollination, that is without the aid of insects, does occur, but it is not enough in itself. In fact, if self-pollination takes place with poor pollen, it is likely to reduce the effect of any visit to the flower by an insect carrying good pollen that might occur later.

As far as the gardener is concerned, it all comes down to what we have said previously; the fullest encouragement of pollinating insects must be allowed. If we are determined to use polythene tunnels, we should plant short rows, so that insects can get in and out of the tunnels freely. This is perhaps especially important where vigorous varieties making masses of leaf are grown.

NUTRITIONAL VALUE OF STRAWBERRIES

In small gardens where space for fruit is limited, preference should be given to fruits having the highest nutritional value. Since vitamin C (ascorbic acid) content is the main nutritional yardstick of fruit, this is the one by which the choice is usually determined. With an average of 17mg ascorbic acid per ounce of fresh fruit, strawberries are second only to blackcurrants (average 60mg oz).

When the value of citrus fruits as an inhibitor of scurvy among seamen became recognised, and when the active agent was found to be the ascorbic acid contained in these, this acid, when it later became known as vitamin C, was called the anti-scurvy vitamin.

Nobody in advanced societies gets scurvy today, but vitamin C is essential for health, and a daily intake of at least 30mg, and preferably 50, is required by adults. It cannot be stored in the body, which is why it is needed in daily doses. Where it is lacking in children, growth becomes checked, gums and mouth may be open to infection, and the children will probably break out in spots, especially if they are allowed to stuff themselves with sweets.

Strawberries contain some carotene, which is converted into vitamin A, or axerophthol, in the body. This, as everyone probably knows, is a visual aid, but it also stiffens resistance to various infections and is essential to growth. It is measured in international units per ounce. Strawberries contain about 4iu/oz, which is infinitesimal when compared to maincrop carrots (5,700iu/oz) but is nevertheless better than none at all.

Riboflavin, essential to human needs, but required in only small quantities, ie about 2mg daily, is present in strawberries in comparatively minute amounts, probably not more than 10 micrograms per ounce.

Nicotinic acid reaches the level of 110 micrograms per ounce, second only to tomatoes, and sharing this place with raspberries. This acid should not be confused with nicotine; although the two have certain chemical similarities, they are not the same, and nicotinic acid, indispensable to healthy skin, sturdy growth and a strong digestion, is not derived from the now much abused nicotine. Strawberries contain about

110 micrograms per ounce, rather less than one hundredth of the daily requirement.

The somewhat mysterious vitamin, Pantothenic Acid, needed in daily amounts of about 12mg is present in strawberries to the value of approximately 65 micrograms per ounce. Its precise function in man is not known, but its lack causes skin defects.

All the above values are average figures; the content of vitamins varies to some extent between varieties, and their values probably fluctuate according to seasonal conditions.

Vitamin C diminishes in the interval between picking and eating the fruit, which is a sound reason for reducing this interval to the minimum. The vitamin is also lost more quickly from damaged fruit and from that kept in warm temperatures. When the fruit is warm, enzymes become active that assist the oxidisation of ascorbic acid into products that are of no value to the human body. When this happens one might as well eat blotting paper as far as nutrition is concerned.

Vitamin C is lost more by cooking fruit slowly at a low temperature than by cooking quickly at a high one, a point that should be remembered when making strawberry jam. This is because the enzymes responsible for speeding up oxidisation are more active at warm that at higher temperatures. Unfortunately much vitamin C is lost from strawberries during jam making no matter what the cooking method may be, but there is no point in losing it all through using the wrong one.

Canned strawberries retain quite a high vitamin C content, and are a valuable source in early spring when fresh produce is comparatively scarce.

PICKING

The beautiful shine of a strawberry is easily spoilt by finger and thumb marks. These marks take time to appear and are obviously of no consequence if one is engaged in that delightful occupation described by Edward Bunyard as 'ambulant consumption', when the transit period of the strawberry from plant to mouth is short. But if strawberries for the table are pulled from the stalks by holding the berries, then by the time they appear before the expectant guest their pristine glory may be a little tarnished by soft pale coloured marks where finger and thumb had imprisoned them. They should be picked with stalks intact. The stalk and calyx can then be removed just before the berries are ready for serving.

XII

Origins and History

Exactly how the strawberry got its name nobody seems to know with certainty, though several likely guesses have been made. The first recorded mention was that of the Anglo-Saxon Aelfric who, some time in the tenth century, referred to Fraga, streaberize, or possibly streawberize, a compound, according to Eric Partridge, of the Old English streaw (straw) and berige (berry).

From the Old English streaw came the Middle English stree, and finally, straw. Webster states that the berry gained its name from being found under mown grass, which might suggest that his etymology was sometimes a trifle hazardous, or that he did not know much about strawberries, for I do not think these are often found in the wild under mown grass.

Ernest Weekly in his *Concise Etymological Dictionary*, 2nd Edition, 1952, mentions 'the tiny strawlike particles which cover the fruit', a rather less concise explanation of the name strawberry than one might expect, since, as we have seen, the strawberry is not technically 'a fruit'.

Another derivation offered is 'straying plant', a reference to the runners that stray from the parent. This idea found expression in Latimer's condemnation of 'strawberry preachers', those peregrinating preachers of the sixteenth century who strayed from their parishes, returning only once a year. 'The preachying of the words of God unto the people is called meate—not strawberries, that come but once a yeare and tarry not longe.'

Latimer's phrase appealed to later churchmen who had cause to chasten their less assiduous brethren, or to condemn the quality of the preaching, for it was still being heard a hundred years after he coined it.

Another version of the strawlike particles theory is 'straw-like stems', which is not terribly convincing, while 'straying berry', has also been suggested as a possible alternative.

These hard working seekers after the origin of the straw-berry's name have all been slapped down in the magisterial manner befitting that august tome, the *Oxford Dictionary of English Etymology*, which puts an end to the matter with the terse observation. 'The reason for the name is unknown'.

Although strawberries were eaten by the Anglo-Saxons, they cannot be considered as being of ancient lineage as far as garden cultivation is concerned, for they seem to have had no place in the horticulture of classical times. Indeed, it is almost a relief to name one fruit which the Romans did not bring to Britain. Nevertheless, in the fourteenth century there were over a thousand plants of the wild strawberry, *Fragaria vesca*, or Wood Strawberry, in the gardens of the Louvre. This and the Hautbois, *F. moschata*, another wild type, indigenous to central Europe, were the two main species grown there for about a century. In 1485 there appeared the first recorded illustration of the strawberry, in the Mainz *Herbarius*.

Similarly in our own country, the Wood Strawberry was the chief type, and this and its several variants remain as our familiar wild species. There were no 'cultivated' kinds; plants for the garden were dug up from their native habitats, and Thomas Tusser, in his *Five Hundred Points of Good Hus-bandrie*, 1557, wrote somewhat peremptorily,

> *Wife into a garden and set me a plot*
> *With strawberry roots, the best to be got.*
> *Such growing abroad among thorns in the wood*
> *Well chosen and picked proved excellent good.*

It is not hard to imagine the rejoinder with which such an order would be met by today's emancipated wives.

But in the words 'the best to be got' and 'well chosen and picked' we discern a nice perception in Master Tusser. The Wood Strawberry is often regarded as producing poor little berries, not worth picking. This is a grave injustice where the best samples are concerned, for these give sweet tasting berries that make first rate jam. There are variants of this wild plant, and differences in berry quality according to soil. The species is widely distributed over Great Britain, occurring on such disparate geological formations as woodland soils, rich in organic matter, and chalk downland. On the latter, the quality is seldom very good, but on the former the plants are usually sturdy and prolific and the berries, though small, are excellent.

In 1430, or thereabout, John Lydgate wrote a song, 'London Lickpenny', in which occurred the line, 'hot pescods one gan cry, strabery rype, and chery in the ryse'. Thus was born the street cry of strawberry ripe, no doubt to be taken up with gusto by the medieval barrow boys. A hundred years later a 'Dyetary' assured its readers that 'rawe crayme vindecocted, eaten with strawberyes or hurtis, is a rural mannes banket'. Hurtis were whortleberries, known for centuries in the hinterland of Surrey and probably elsewhere as hurts. From the name perhaps came Hurtwood Common, where these wild berries abound—or where they abounded when I lived in Surrey, but that was long ago, and they have probably since been buried under acres of concrete.

Then in 1620 came a strong hint that garden cultivation could improve the quality of strawberries; 'the wilde or voluntary strawberries are not so good as those that are manured in gardens.' Seventy years later that great rural observer, and man for all seasons, John Evelyn, noted in his *Kalender of Horticulture* that 'you can hardly over-water your Strawberry Beds in a dry season'. With the final spelling of strawberry had come a basic appreciation of the plants' needs.

The progenitors of the cultivated forms are two primary wild types, the Virginian, *Fragaria virginiana*, and the Chilian or Beach Strawberry, *F. chiloensis*. Both are American, the first perhaps mainly of North America, but not entirely so. It is also known as the Scarlet Strawberry, and is found at altitudes from sea level to 12,000ft. It produces variable characters, some of sufficient distinction to warrant classification as a species, as in the type found in the prairies of Illinois, and known as *F. Ioensis* or *Illinoensis*.

It was the Virginian and its variants which fed the pioneers who 'pushed westward, in parallel lines, occupying successively western New York, Michigan, Illinois, Kentucky, Ohio and the great Mississippi Valley. The wild strawberries everywhere greeted them with an abundance of fresh fruit—a most welcome addition to frontier fare. The wild strawberry refreshed the "forty-niners" of California and those who followed the Lewis and Clark trail. It has brought cheer to the settlers of the last frontiers in Manitoba and Alaska. 'Always the wild strawberry has been intimately and gratefully associated with pioneer life.' So wrote S. W. Fletcher in *The Strawberry in North America*.

The Chilian Strawberry has a much wider geographical range, extending from the Pacific coast of North and South America to the Western slopes of the Rocky Mountains, the Andes, and certain Pacific islands.

It, too, is variable, but the best forms produce large berries, and these had been selected for cultivation by the Chilean Indians before the white man reached America. It is recorded that the largest berries were the size of walnuts, and this species did in fact give the biggest berries of the genus until the recently introduced giant types from the continent.

In approximately 1712 a French officer, Amedeé Francois Frezier, who evidently had an eye to business, took a number of plants back to France, of which all but five died on the journey, owing, it was said, to lack of fresh water.

It is a habit of the Chilian species to produce some plants having only female flowers, and it so happened that all the five surviving plants were of this type. One was planted at Plougastil among other species that bore male flowers which effected pollination of the female ones on the new sample. From this new one stocks were eventually established, and a flourishing strawberry business emerged, to export many strawberries to England from about the late 1850s.

The remaining four plants, put in elsewhere, apparently

had no pollinating partners, for although they flowered they remained fruitless.

Later on, the young French botanist Antoine Nicholas Duchesne (1747-1827) planted the Virginian and probably the Hautbois, which he named *F. moschata*, among subsequent introductions of the type brought back by Frezier, thus overcoming the pollination problem.

Several 'perfect' types, ie plants bearing both male and female flowers and therefore self-fertile, arose from raising crosses between Duchesne's plantings, of which the most famous was the Pine Strawberry, first known as the *Fraiser-ananas*, later named *F. ananassa* by Duchesne. A century or so later descendants of this were being raised in England under such names as Bicton Pine, Frogmore Late Pine and Stirling Castle Pine. The species is also known as *F. grandiflora*.

Duchesne was a most gifted man who, at the early age of nineteen, published his *Histoire naturelle des Fraisiers,* which remains a standard work on the origins of cultivated strawberries.

Perhaps some of the more mature botanists of his day were a trifle jealous of this youthful success, for they argued that the *Fraisier-ananas* was an introduction from North America, but Duchesne maintained, correctly in the view of modern plant breeders, that it was a hybrid from his crossing of the Chilian with the Virginian. So these two are now firmly accepted as the parents of modern cultivated strawberries.

In addition to the various wild types found in many parts of the world there was the Alpine Strawberry, *F. vesca semperflorens* so named, I think, by the Swiss naturalist Conrad Gesner (1516-1556). In its several varieties this was a long established favourite among connoisseurs in Great Britain, but between Gesner's time and its introduction into our country some two centuries elapsed.

In the 1870s French raisers were concentrating on these alpines and on perpetual fruiting types, varieties that fruited more or less continually from about June to October, or even later, or which bore their major crops in autumn. A few were introduced, but none proved of much value until, after many disappointments, the Abbé Thivolet of Chenôves in Saône-et-Loire, produced his famous Saint-Joseph in 1893. Many more perpetuals were raised over the ensuing years, yet it was not until the 1930s that really good types, having both vigour and fruitfulness, appeared. Notable among introductions of that decade were La Sans Rivale and Triomphe, raised by M Chapron of Caen.

The very odd thing about the quite considerable number of perpetuals that have appeared in France over the past thirty years or so is that extremely few seem to have appeared in English nurseries, though as we have seen in the section on varieties, there is now a fairly good list of new kinds from the continent. Some may have derived from the French types of the thirties and onwards, but the fact that these themselves have not become established here is a little mystifying, especially as some are quite excellent, like M Maillochon's Saint-Hubert, which is a lovely rose colour and of very fine flavour.

It is rather an astonishing fact that in spite of all this continental activity on behalf of strawberry raising, the first variety to earn wide recognition in England and to be taken up for general cultivation did not appear until about 1814, when the Isleworth market gardener, Michael Keens, produced his famous Imperial. From this followed his Seedling, about 1823.

Both were large fruited seedlings of *F. chiloensis*, of a kind not previously known. In 1823 production was particularly good, and marked possibly the most important stage of strawberry raising then reached in England. The Royal Horticultural Society presented Keens with a silver cup, and included a coloured plate of the strawberry in their Transactions, which was perhaps an even greater honour.

Keens Seedling, the large size and excellent flavour of which 'created a sensation which probably no succeeding strawberry has ever equalled', may fairly be regarded as the foundation of the large fruited variety in this country.

The tardy recognition, until Keens came on the scene, of the potential which strawberry breeding offered is all the more surprising when we realise that Philip Miller, of *Gardeners' Dictionary* fame, brought the Chilian variety to this country as early as 1727, and added to it in 1760 by introducing the Pine.

However, Philip Miller had set the pace, and in the following years Thomas Andrew Knight (1759-1838), one of the most illustrious of all plant breeders, raised over four hundred seedlings. Sir Joseph Paxton heightened the interest by naming fourteen species of strawberry when he brought out his *Botanical Dictionary* in 1840. In 1862 Bradley raised the strawberry that he named after this great man, and until its demise within comparatively recent times it was judged by many people as the finest variety of all time.

But perhaps the pinnacle of 19th century strawberry raising was reached by Thomas Laxton, whose firm lives on to this day, albeit in amalgamation with another, also a giant in its day, namely Bunyard & Son. Laxton raised the Royal Sovereign in 1892, a variety that is as much a household word as the Cox's Orange apple. The present firm reckon it still 'The Cream of Strawberries'. It is doubtful whether any summer fruiting variety can beat it at its best, though it has to be admitted that its best is not easy to achieve.

APPENDICES

Appendix I

APPROVED CHEMICALS

Inasmuch as the pest, disease and weed control chemicals listed in this book are perfectly safe for garden use if used to maker's instructions, mention of the Approval Scheme of the Ministry of Agriculture may seem unnecessary. Nevertheless, confusion is possible, because brand names do not always convey an immediate description of the chemical, and even the small print may leave the purchaser in some doubt as to the safety of the spray. Proprietary products can be officially approved, and gardeners are strongly urged to use only those that have been passed by the Ministry. Approval is indicated by the letter A stamped on the container, surmounted by a crown, and with words Agricultural Chemicals Approval Scheme at its base.

Appendix II

COMPATIBILITY OF SPRAYS

It is sometimes necessary to combine different materials in one spray application. The extent to which this can be done with garden sprayers is obviously more limited than it is with large machines used in fruit farming, but the possibility of mixed sprays still exists for gardeners where the tackle is able to cope with an increased density of material. This problem is simply a mechanical one. There is another, which relates to possible chemical reaction between different materials, bringing undesirable results.

Among the materials I have mentioned there is almost complete compatibility. A possible exception is a malathion-captan combination, which should be avoided. Gardeners who rely on my recommendations will not use lime sulphur; I do not deplore this spray—in fact it is an excellent fungicide—but I have not recommended it because it can have somewhat caustic effects, whereas the alternatives mentioned do not. Nevertheless, it is relatively cheap, and this fact alone might encourage its use. If it is used, it should not be combined with captan or dinocap (as it might be, on a half and half basis to reduce the cost of the latter two) or with foliar feeds, or with manganese sulphate or any copper containing spray.

There would be no point in including any of the nutrient sprays, eg urea, magnesium sulphate etc with a proprietary foliar feed, since the latter would contain these elements. Except for iron sprays, which should not be mixed with other substances, the other 'straight' nutrients mentioned can be mixed with each other, provided the sprayer will take them, and that the nozzle can cope with them without getting blocked. Often these conditions cannot be met, especially with urea plus magnesium sulphate.

179

Appendix III

A SPECIMEN SPRAY PROGRAMME

In offering a specimen spray programme for pest and disease control, I want to emphasise that this is not meant to be taken as an annual routine. My hope is that what has been said on this subject will make clear the fact that there is no yearly routine applicable to spraying. Conditions vary from season to season, and measures needed one year may be quite different from those needed the following year; in some seasons no spraying may be necessary.

The table is only a guide, but in fact it covers virtually all the major controllable pests and preventable diseases that most gardeners are likely to encounter in probably four years out of five. I hope the fifth will not bring devastation. It should not, if the relatively simple procedures advocated earlier are followed.

Period	Material	Pest or Disease	Remarks
Late April	Derris or Pyrethrum	Aphids	If red spider mites are present, use either derris or malathion. In either case, watch results and repeat if necessary, 5–7 days later.
	Pyrethrum	Blossom Weevil Tortrix Caterpillars	If red spider mites are present, add derris.
	Dinocap	Mildew	Mainly needed in hot, dry weather.
Early to mid-May	Dinocap	Mildew	This is normally the first spray. Repeat as necessary at 10–14 day intervals.
Early Blossom	Thiram or Captan or Benomyl	Greymould	Spray *must* go on at first flower. Repeat 10 days later, and again in wet or humid weather. Avoid further spraying if fruit is to be canned. In some seasons 'early blossom' may coincide with mid-May spray
Immediately Post-Flower	Nicotine or Dicofol	Tarsonemid Mites	
Post-Harvest	Nicotine or Dicofol	Tarsonemid Mites	

INDEX